TALES TOLD BY FOSSILS

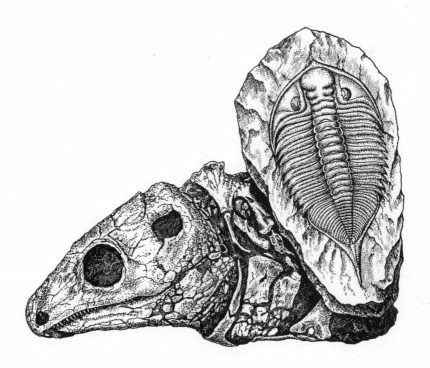

By Carroll Lane Fenton

TALES TOLD BY FOSSILS
OUR AMAZING EARTH
OUR LIVING WORLD

By Carroll Lane Fenton and Mildred Adams Fenton

GIANTS OF GEOLOGY
IN PREHISTORIC SEAS
THE LAND WE LIVE ON
OUR CHANGING WEATHER
PREHISTORIC ZOO
THE ROCK BOOK
ROCKS AND THEIR STORIES
THE FOSSIL BOOK

One of the largest titanotheres and a species of creodont, a primitive carnivore. Both lived on prairies of the West some 30 million years ago.

TALES TOLD BY
FOSSILS

Carroll Lane Fenton

DOUBLEDAY & COMPANY, INC., GARDEN CITY, NEW YORK
1966

Library of Congress Catalog Card Number 66–11731
Copyright © 1966 by Carroll Lane Fenton
All Rights Reserved
Printed in the United States of America

CONTENTS

TALES TOLD BY FOSSILS

A preparator removes rock from a slab of petrified bones at the Museum of Paleontology of the University of California, Berkeley.

1 UNEARTHING LIFE'S PAST

ONE DAY IN 1897, a young man named Walter Granger rode across a plain in southeastern Wyoming. Far south of him rose a ridge known as Como Bluff; northward the land dipped into a shallow valley, or "draw," that led to the Little Medicine Bow River. At the head of the draw stood a half-ruined cabin built by a sheep herder. Ground around it was littered with rusty-brown boulders.

Granger was collecting fossils for the then-young American Museum of Natural History, in New York City. He soon saw that the boulders were more than lumps of stone; they were battered, weather-beaten bones of big dinosaurs. Other bones, not so badly worn, formed the lower walls of the cabin. All had come from shaly sandstone that formed the surrounding land.

The collector examined both boulders and sandstone; then he reported that Bone Cabin Draw contained a rich deposit of dinosaurian fossils. Collecting began the following spring, and Granger soon found the right hind leg of a reptile whose limbs had been unknown. Work continued through six summers, into the autumn of 1903. By that time the Bone Cabin deposit had yielded 483 portions of varied dinosaurs, as well as remains of turtles and crocodiles. These specimens formed the greatest collection of fossil reptile remains ever taken from a single locality.

But before we go further, what are fossils?

We frequently think of fossils as prehistoric plants and animals that have been "turned into stone," or petrified. Many fossils are not stony, however, and many that are have not been petrified. An acceptable definition must provide for both types, and it should do more than tell us that fossils lived before human beings learned to write down facts of history or carve them on stone. That first happened about 5300 years ago, but most fossils are so much more than 5300 years old that their great antiquity should be indicated.

Some inclusive definitions are long, but these demands can be met without wordiness or technicality. An adequate definition says that *fossils are remains or traces of things that lived during ancient geologic times and were buried in rocks that settled on the earth's outer portion, or crust.* This statement will serve us well if we bear in mind three facts:

First, *ancient geologic times* began with the earliest ages that can be traced in rocks and extended through the epoch that directly followed the last great Ice Age. In years, this means from perhaps 3,500,000,000 to about 10,000 B.C. As yet, however, few fossils have been found in rocks more than 1800 million years old.

Second, *rocks* are not necessarily *stones*. Most rocks that covered ancient plants and animals were soil, sand, mud, or other loose materials. Many of these have become hard stones, but some are almost as far from being solid as they ever were. Countless fossils lie

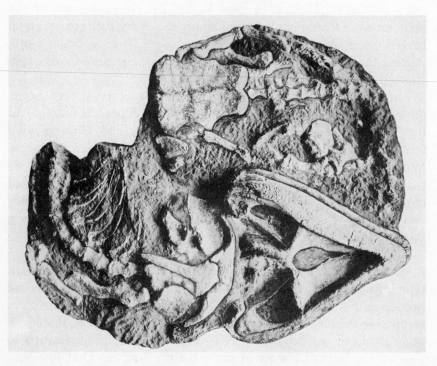

Remains of a reptile from the Permian Red Beds of Texas. These bones are exceptionally well preserved.

in sands or clays that crumble in our hands though they are 20, 40, or even 440 million years old.

Third, most scientists who write about very ancient men use the word "fossilized" to mean *petrified*. When one of these authors says that a skull has not been fossilized he means only that it has not become stony. It still may be old enough to rank as a fossil.

Some rocks have changed little; others have solidified or have been remade. Similarly, some fossils are much as they were when they were alive, others retain only a little once-living material, and many have none at all. Some shells, for example, still show color patterns; ancient mammoths that were frozen in icy ground retain their flesh, skin, and hair. Many leaves, however, are thin films of carbon that remained after most of their original substance had decayed. Other leaves are mere impressions left in soft mud or sand which then hardened. Footprints are impressions, too, but most fossil burrows are solidified sand that filled holes dug by worms and other small animals.

All these, however, are less abundant than petrified remains. Most of the latter are shells or other hard coverings, but many are bones or wood. They have been filled or replaced by stony material that may be harder than the rock around them. This explains why petrified fossils often "weather out" and lie on the ground while rocks that once covered them disappear.

Collecting Fossils

Though fossils have been preserved in many ways, each of them tells its part in the story of life during ancient geologic times. It is to discover this story that museums and individuals collect and study fossils. Big ones are brought in by expeditions; to dig up and pack a dinosaur or mammoth is a job for many hands. Seven skilled collectors and scientists worked at Bone Cabin in 1899, with help from pick-and-shovel men and teamsters. An expedition to Asia, for plants, animals, and rocks, as well as for fossils, had a staff of scientists, technicians, artists, photographers, mechanics, and even camel drivers, since camel trains carried gasoline for trucks and passenger cars. Hair pulled from the camels as they shed was used in packing specimens.

Large expeditions have made great discoveries, but small ones are important, too. Many fine skeletons have been found by three or four

men on horseback, with a wagon for camp gear and specimens. Today, a Jeep takes the place of horses, and one truck does the work
of several wagons. A truck may also carry a "field party" composed
of a single professor and a few of his advanced students. Shells and
other small fossils may be found by a professor, student, or museum
collector alone, or by salesmen, engineers, and office workers. These
amateurs—and their wives—often belong to clubs of "rockhounds" to
whom collecting trips provide outings on weekends and holidays.

Most expeditions go far afield; clubs and individual collectors usually work near home. They do so because they have limited time,
and because fossil beds often lie in the midst of civilization. Ravines
close to Minneapolis, for example, have been worn through beds
that contain ancient snails and clams, as well as other marine creatures. Sea shells are common in Cincinnati, where they lie on every
hillside and in almost every ditch. Corals weather out of shaly pas-
tures in western New York; crinoids, or sea lilies, are found in quarries where limestone is crushed as fertilizer for Iowa cornfields. Bones
of Ice-age mammals underlie a park in Los Angeles. Though these
fossils are not available to collectors, they may be examined by anyone who walks down a spiral ramp into the bone deposit.

Ice-age Angeleños include mammoths and giant lions; 45-foot
reptiles once swam where suburbs now stand in New Jersey; bones
of ground sloths 10 feet long have been dug from farms in Ohio.
But such oversized creatures are exceptions, for most fossils within
reach of home-based collectors are small. Even the white sharks of
ancient Maryland are not big fossils; though the fish once were 40 to
50 feet long, their only remains are petrified teeth 4 to 8 inches in
length.

Small size, however, does not mean that a fossil is unimportant.
The oldest known plants are so tiny that they can be seen only
through a microscope, and few corals, shells, or sea lilies are big. Indeed, specimens less than 6 inches in length tell most of life's story
during its first 1300 million years. Even when large plants and animals became common, small species outnumbered giants by many
thousands to one.

Besides being more plentiful than big ones, small fossils are eas-
ier to handle. We realize this when we see how two collectors obtain
and "prepare" their specimens.

The first collector is out for ancient sea shells and corals. For an
hour or two he works on slabs of limestone, splitting them with a

chisel and a geologist's pick. When he finds a fossil, he breaks it out, taking care to leave some rock around it. After wrapping it in news-paper, he puts the specimen into his knapsack or a carton which he can carry to his car.

Above the limestone are layers of shale which rains have reduced to clay. Here the collector stoops low or crawls, picking up specimens that lie on the surface and prying others out of the ground. Most of these go into paper bags; those that are especially delicate are wrapped in tissue paper or cotton and placed in small boxes or wide-mouthed bottles. Tiny fossils that are abundant may be scooped up or swept into bags with a whisk broom.

When this collector returns to his laboratory or basement work-room, he chips excess rock from the fossils that were found in lime-stone. Those from shale are washed to soften their coating of clay; any that still clings to them is removed with a stiff brush, a needle, or a knife. If the fossils are delicate, this work may be done under a magnifier.

The second collector, who is seeking big vertebrates, may begin by spying the tip of a bone that projects from shale or sandstone. With his pick he uncovers a few more bones; if they show that the fossil is worth taking out, he removes just enough rock to show where it lies and where he must dig to obtain it without damage. Only after this has been done can he begin to remove his specimen.

This requires skill and great care, for even the hardest petrified bones seldom are very strong. Our collector of vertebrates must know when to change from pick or crowbar to chisel; when to lay the chisel aside in favor of scraper and brush. He works till he knows where his specimen ends; then he cuts a trench around it and removes the rock beneath. As he does so, assistants set up a small derrick and equip it with block and tackle. With them the collector and his helpers will lift rock and fossil out of the ground.

Here we get ahead of the story—much too far ahead. As bone after bone is exposed, it is covered with tissue paper and soaked with shellac or some chemical preservative. Cracks may be cemented; splints of wood or steel are placed upon weak or shattered blocks of stone. Strips of cloth dipped in wet plaster of Paris are then spread over splints, fossil, and rock, crossing and recrossing until the mass is rigidly bound together. Not until the plaster hardens can the fossil be raised and boxed for shipment.

When box and contents reach the museum, the splints and bandages are removed. Skilled preparators then cut away excess rock, working first with small hammers and chisels, and finally with dentist's drills. Bones that still are intact need only be cleaned; those shattered since they became fossils are pieced together bit by bit and then are put away for study or are assembled into skeletons. These, in turn, must be supported by plaster and bars or tubes of metal so they can be displayed.

Sometimes this process must be reversed, and skeletons that have been "mounted" are taken down for study or repair. Sometimes, too, bones that have been assembled from fragments are then separated for examination. The results may suggest skulls or vertebrae of modern animals that have been taken apart for anatomical study. But no modern skull is as hard to take apart as one that has been in the ground for millions upon millions of years.

2 WHAT FOSSILS REVEAL

FOSSILS RECORD the story of life during past ages. But is that record adequate? Do fossils give the facts we need to construct a reliable, well-rounded account?

Some critics who ask these questions give a negative reply. Most fossil animals, they say, are merely petrified hard parts: bones, shells, or crustlike coats from which all living material has vanished. Petrified wood is no better; moreover, most ancient plants are known from leaves which are either black films of carbon or impressions in sandstone or shale. Some reptiles survive only as footprints, and worms have been described from solidified sand that filled their burrows. Such fossils do not even show the shapes of creatures that made them.

With some exceptions these statements are true; no one who works with fossils denies them. It is equally true that most of the things that lived during past ages did not become fossils when they died. Countless creatures without hard parts decayed; so did the vast majority of seaweeds and soft, herbaceous land-plants. Fish and four-footed animals met the same fate unless their remains were soon covered by fine sand or mud. Creatures of rocky seashores vanished as waves smashed their shells into bits too small for recognition. Waves also destroyed tracks and burrows, and shifting rivers swept away many footprints that had been left on muddy sand.

Fossils are the remains and traces that escaped this wholesale destruction. No one can estimate their number, but they must be only a tiny fraction of the total that lived and died during the past two billion years. This fact, like the imperfection of remains and traces that were preserved, seems to support the critics who say that fossils really tell very little of life's story during the long geologic past.

Still, the record is much better than words alone imply. It is true that hordes of ancient organisms lived, died, and disappeared—but it is equally true that other hordes were buried in rocks and became fos-

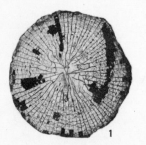  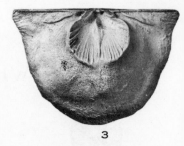

1 and 2 are sections cut through fossil corals; they show structures built by the creatures' soft bodies; 3, the interior of a lamp-shell, bears the "scars" to which muscles were attached.

sils. Limy algae fill beds 10 to 100 feet thick that extend across scores of miles. Coral banks are quite as extensive; oysterlike shells are so abundant that collectors gather hundreds in a day. With very small fossils the number increases to thousands, and even big fossils are not always rare. Visitors to the Petrified Forest, in northern Arizona, may climb one hillock and look down on hundreds of stony logs. In Montana, one collector found remains of some 500 skulls that belonged to a single type of dinosaur.

Not only are many fossils abundant; they exist in great variety. Among plants they range from the simplest algae to trees and highly specialized grasses. Animals range from sponges to whales among sea-dwellers, and from worms to human beings on land. There is also a vast array of one-celled creatures called protozoans, which seem to belong to several kingdoms distinct from both plants and animals.

Most of these fossils are petrified—but instead of being meaningless fragments, they are often preserved in amazing and very meaningful detail. Many skeletons contain almost every bone. A fossil coral may look like a stone, but its interior is an orderly maze of ridges and plates arranged in a pattern which shows the nature and relationships of the soft-bodied animal that made them. Ancient shells reveal the fibers and grains of which they are made, as well as ridges, frills, spines, and bosses on their surfaces. Cell walls are preserved in much petrified wood, as well as in a surprising number of ferns and small herbaceous plants. There also are threadlike fungi so small that their nature is hardly apparent until they are greatly magnified.

Such details are lacking from films of carbon and impressions in

Carbonized fossils of Middle Cambrian age, perhaps 550 million years old. Number 1, a marine worm, preserves the shape of the body and spines on its surface; 2 is a wormlike creature with skin, head, spines, and legs; 3, a relative of the trilobites, shows both shape and internal organs.

sandstone or shale. Yet impressions show the shapes and veins of leaves as clearly as do modern plants that are pressed and kept for scientific study. Impressions of shells, small skulls, and bones are so clear that they can be reproduced in plaster or modeling compounds and examined almost as if they were petrified. Many fossil insects and spiders also are impressions, as are wing membranes of flying reptiles and feathers of the earliest birds. Dinosaur "mummies" contain petrified bones, but their rough skins are impressions in sand that covered the sun-dried carcasses and hardened into stone. Virtually all fossil jellyfish are imprints, yet they show organs in the once-watery bodies. They also are exceptions to the rule that animals without hard parts have not become fossils.

Most carbonized fossils show little more than impressions. But marine reptiles from Europe and fish from northern Ohio preserve carbonized shapes of bodies and fins, as well as skin that sometimes is darker on the sides and back than it is below. Much older fossils from the Canadian Rockies include carbonized seaweeds, small "shellfish" whose digestive systems show plainly, and worms with fleshy snouts and hooked or bristly spines. Soft-bodied parasitic flatworms have been found in carbonized insects.

The complaint that petrified fossils preserve only hard parts must also be qualified. Whole fairy shrimps and spiders have been found, as well as insects, slugs, a reptile head complete with eyes, and even the fleshy breast of a bird. The fairy shrimps, which are fresh-water crustaceans, include females whose pouches are full of eggs. Some insects show well-preserved muscles and minute tubes that once carried air through the bodies. Other insects include pupae and soft-bodied caterpillars as well as adults.

Even these fossils are surpassed by some spiders in amber and spores in cannel coal. The former preserve leg muscles, internal organs, and cells in the body wall; silk spun 30 million years ago still leads from spinnerets. Spores, which are reproductive cells of plants such as ferns, contain nuclei that served as centers of life when the cells were jellylike protoplasm. In some nuclei are chromosomes whose beadlike sections once were clusters of genes, the particles which would have determined both hereditary structure and appearance had the spores lived to become new plants.

The most nearly perfect large fossils are those of mammoths that were frozen in ground ice of Siberia and Alaska. They include bones, tendons, flesh, skin, and dried blood; half-chewed food lies between the teeth and partly digested meals fill the stomachs. Such remains are much more revealing than the dried carcasses and deposits of dung that are sometimes found in desert caves.

Still fossils need not include hair or soft parts in order to give information about them. Varied bivalves, for example, bear scars made by muscles that closed or opened the shells. Channels show where watery blood flowed through flesh; curved lines record the position of tubes that brought food into ancient clams. Bones show that some reptiles had paddle-shaped flippers, though the legs of other reptiles looked like fins.

Among vertebrates, most muscles are fastened to bones. Marks on petrified bones show the positions, shapes, and sizes of muscles that operated parts ranging from tails and legs to jaws. When these muscles are restored on paper or in modeling clay, they reveal the proportions of ancient animals, the attitudes they could assume, and movements that could be made by head, neck, and legs. Such evidence is the basis of reconstructions which show fossil vertebrates as they looked while they were alive.

Skulls reveal the size, shape, and structure of brains, as well as nerves that once led from them. In fact, we have a surprising amount of information about the sensory, mental, and motor equipment of creatures ranging from armored pre-fish to men. Some fishlike agnaths, for example, felt heat and cold and heard low sounds by means of nerve-endings distributed along channels, or canals, that crisscrossed bony armor on the head and forward part of the body. Cavities holding the brains of flying reptiles show that these creatures had a poor sense of smell but were able to see very well. Big dinosaurs had such large bodies and such small, inefficient brains that their legs and tails were largely controlled by greatly enlarged nerve-knots, or ganglia, between the shoulders and above the hips. The earliest men, who ranged from Africa to Europe and across Asia, possessed small skulls with low foreheads, which show that their brains were neither as large nor as efficient as ours. Still, these poor brains seem to have furnished the mental requirements for speech.

All living things grow, and many change greatly as they do so. Series of petrified skulls and skin-crusts trace the development of several ancient animals from larvae or unhatched eggs to adults. One famous series of skulls traces growth of the head in horned dinosaurs whose partly developed eggs were found in what is now Mongolia.

Series of petrified shells form similar records, but snails, clams, and lamp-shells (or brachiopods) preserved changes in size, shape, and surface ornamentation on their individual shells. Thus a snail that began by covering its body with a smooth, twisted cap soon added a coil with cross ribs and then built whorls with spiral ridges. Last came a narrow channel that extended far forward, covering a fleshy tube that took water into the body. Lines formed when growth stopped for a while show how both clams and brachiopods changed shape as they grew up and then became old. On many shells, these changes were accompanied by new types of ornamentation.

Accidents and disease were common in the past, just as they are today. Some petrified trees show partly healed burns; bones and shells contain healed breaks; legs and even parts of the body were bitten from turtles and from jointed animals very distantly related to crabs. Logs bear lumps caused by fungous and other diseases; bones reveal tumors, abscesses, inflammation of the marrow, and the results of rheumatism and arthritis. Ancient men suffered from tuberculosis of the spine, rheumatism, ulcerated teeth and jaws, and infected wounds.

Fossils also reveal the surroundings, or environments, of ancient

A honeycomb coral preserves structures built as the animals grew.

Interior of a mollusk shell, showing marks made by muscles and other soft parts.

Veins as well as shape appear in this impression of a sycamore leaf.

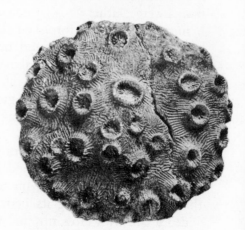

A colonial coral, showing ridges built by the individual animals.

organisms. Trees undoubtedly lived on land, but seaweeds must have grown in salt water. All living corals, scallops, and whales are marine; we infer that their fossil relatives also lived in seas and oceans. On the other hand, fossils related to living fresh-water fish, snails, and mussels are assigned to ancient streams, lakes, and ponds. Ice-age mastodons often waded into swamps while feeding, for their bones are now found where they were mired. Ancient ground sloths were just what their name says, for their size (some were 20 feet long) shows that they could not live in trees, as their modern relatives do.

Many fossils record the climatic conditions under which they

Annual rings, rays, and evidence of disease in a piece of petrified wood from Idaho.

These fossil shells (*Exogyra*) grew upon one another, as modern oysters do.

Brachiopods cover this slab of shale. The arrow points to a boring made by a snail.

This delicate coral grew on a sea bottom of fine, hard mud that settled very slowly.

lived. Woolly mammoths whose carcasses lie in ground ice plainly experienced a climate as cold as that of central Siberia today. Big dinosaurs, on the other hand, could live only where warm weather lasted the year round. Palms and breadfruit trees required warm to tropical climates, and their fossils in Spitsbergen and Greenland mean that those regions were virtually tropical. Coal-age trees probably needed less heat, but their lack of annual rings is evidence that all seasons were essentially alike.

A variety of evidence shows how ancient animals behaved. Slim sharks must have been swift swimmers, but skates spent most of their time on the bottom, eating creatures which they found in sand or mud. Specimens with impressions of flesh show that fossils known as belemnoids looked, swam, and caught prey like present-day squids. When a squid is attacked, it ejects a cloud of inky liquid that seems to blind enemies. It really paralyzes their organs of smell, so they cannot follow their intended victim. Ink bags in fossils show that belemnoids also used this method of defense.

Ancient barnacles, as well as oysters and mollusks related to them, often attached themselves to shells. Clams of several kinds burrowed into sunken logs, in which their fossils are found today. Some snails crawled in sand as they hunted for food; the marks they left are easily told from the work of worms that swallowed mud or sand, digested whatever food it contained, and left the refuse behind as they burrowed. These fossils also differ from those made by worms which cast leftover mud on the sea bottom, much as modern earthworms leave castings on land.

Several modern snails bore holes into other snails or clams, insert a rasping tongue, and devour their victims alive. Similar borings are found in fossils ranging from 2 to 430 million years in age. Other snails clung to the tops of sea lilies, or crinoids, and fed upon the wastes of their hosts. The petrified shells fit the crinoids to which some are still attached.

These snails took their food as it came, but many vertebrates were active hunters. Carnivorous dinosaurs followed victims by walking or running on their hind legs—only footprints of hind feet are preserved, and petrified bones show that the forelegs were too short to reach the ground. Some of these creatures left broken teeth among the bones of their prey, and at least one carnivore stepped into the footprints of an herbivore which it was stalking. Herbivores fed on plants —but petrified stomach contents show that at least one plant-eating dinosaur also swallowed bony animals. Perhaps it got them without knowing, as it gulped leaves.

Several marine reptiles and fish swallowed food whole, for the undigested remains have been found. A few fish choked to death when meals stuck in their throats; others apparently were killed by their victims' final struggles. That seems to have been the fate of one 14-foot relative of the tarpon, for it died soon after swallowing a fish 5 feet 7 inches in length. But a reptile seemingly swam away and sought other food after biting into the shell of a creature distantly related to the modern nautilus.

Some animals never leave their own home ranges, but many strong

The fly in amber (left) shows hairs on the legs and facets in the eyes. (Photo by F. M. Carpenter) The fossil fish (right) preserves an outline of the body as well as hundreds of small bones.

swimmers travel long distances. About 80 million years ago, a marine reptile swallowed some pink pebbles in the region where Minnesota, Iowa, and South Dakota now meet. The creature then swam at least 400 miles, for his petrified bones—and the pink pebbles—were discovered in western Kansas.

There is no reason to think that this reptile followed an established pattern when it swam to what now is Kansas. But "devils' corkscrews" of northwestern Nebraska tell a different story. These fossils are hardened fillings of burrows dug by land-dwelling beavers; each filling is a spiral that goes several feet into the ground and then becomes an upward-slanting tunnel with a slightly enlarged sleeping chamber at the end. The whole structure seems to represent an inherited pattern like the one that leads fiddler crabs of today's Pacific coast to dig deep burrows with one or two branches ending in small chambers. It is hardly too much to call the devil's corkscrew the fossilized instinct of an animal that lived some 15 million years ago.

These beds of shale near Green River, Utah, settled one upon another in a lake whose basin sank during millions of years. Index fossils show that the lake existed during the Eocene Epoch.

3 BUILDING EARTH'S TIME SCALE

LET US NOW return to the hill where a collector is getting invertebrate fossils from limestone and shale. These rocks lie in layers and beds, or strata, in the order in which they were formed. The first and oldest bed, therefore, is found at the bottom; the latest and youngest appears at the top. Our collector gathers his fossils in this order and labels them according to the beds from which they were taken. If he likes, he may arrange them in a series that will record the history of animals while rocks in the hill were accumulating.

This history will not be long, for the hill is not very high. The record may also fit only one region, for rocks settled in different surroundings and at different times in varied areas. Still, series can be pieced together—not merely from one place to another, but from continent to continent and through deposits of all the ages during which plants, animals, and other organisms have become plentiful fossils. The result, extended by facts obtained from rocks, is a time scale of life's—and earth's—history that embraces more than 3000 million years.

This use of fossils to build a time scale depends on two principles that have been tested for more than 150 years. The first principle states that living things changed with the passing of time, so that some fossils of any period or epoch differ from those of every other. The second principle reverses the first; since fossils differ in rocks of different ages, rocks that contain similar fossils formed at about the same time.

With a diagram, we can use these rules to build up part of our scale. Each column in the diagram represents the rocks exposed in a single slope, hillside, or quarry. Each column, or geologic section, is divided in part by the nature of its rocks, but chiefly by *index fossils* which are found in different beds or formations. Because space is limited, our diagram shows only one index fossil in each bed.

No section duplicates any other, but sections do overlap. At the top of Section 1, for example, beds of limestone contain a sea urchin that also appears in Sections 2, 3, and 7. We therefore match, or correlate, these beds of limestone as well as the shale that lies below them.

Above the limestone in Sections 2, 3, and 7 lie cross-bedded sandstones which seem to belong to a single formation. Section 2 shows that they do, for in it the sandstones are covered by beds which there as well as in Section 7 contain shells related to oysters. Shells of a different type enable us to correlate the fifth bed in Section 7 with one near the base of Section 4. Other shells permit us to match beds in Sections 5 and 6 and so complete our composite section, which extends from the bottom of Section 1 to the top of 6.

This, too, is a limited series, which formed during a small portion

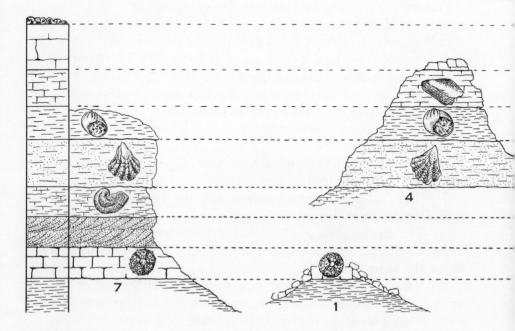

How index fossils are used to build up a geologic section, which is shown at the left without its fossils.

of the earth's history. But by matching fossils the series can be extended until it includes deposits that are still settling and many others that accumulated during the very ancient past. The final product, as we have said, is a record of earth's history that extends through more than 3000 million years.

This record can be put into words—words that already fill many books. The tale can also be condensed into a two-page time scale. This scale divides the past into eras, ages, periods and epochs, mentions some of the things that lived during those times, and notes changes that took place on the earth. Like the rocks in a geologic section, these time divisions are shown with the first (oldest) at the bottom and the last (youngest) at the top. Each division is given a name, just as we name periods and epochs of human history.

But remember: These are geologic eras and ages, not ages established in years. Fossils can tell us that one rock formation was deposited in Early Cambrian times, another during the Eocene Epoch,

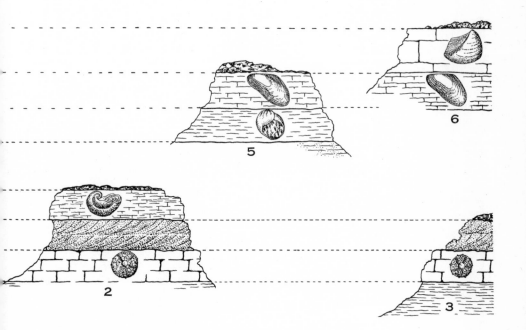

Numbers 1 to 7 show the beds in individual exposures. They are matched, or correlated, by their different fossils.

A TIME SCALE OF EARTH HISTORY

Eras	Periods and Epochs		When They Began	Changes in Lands, Seas, and Living Things
CENOZOIC or Era of Mammals	Quaternary Period	Recent Epoch	8,000 to about 10,000 years ago.	Great glaciers melted for the last time; climates grew warm. Many large land mammals died out near end of epoch. Marine animals began to live in their present homes.
		Pleistocene Epoch, also called the Great Ice Age	One million years ago (old system of division); 2.5 to 3 million years on new system.	Glaciers repeatedly spread over much of Europe, Asia, and North America. Climates and seas were cold when glaciers spread, but warm during interglacial times. Mammals grew large and varied; man evolved.
	Tertiary Period	Pliocene Epoch	13 million	High mountains, including the Rockies, formed as this period began; the Andes, Alps, Cascades, and Himalayas rose in later epochs. Seas seldom covered much of the continents. Mammals became common and varied on land; sharks and bony fish were plentiful. Modern types of corals, clams, snails, etc. became dominant in seas; ammonoids and belemnoids died out but squids and octopi became common. Land plants became more and more like those of the present day.
		Miocene Epoch	25 million	
		Oligocene Epoch	36 million	
		Eocene Epoch	58 million	
		Paleocene Epoch	63 or more million years ago	
MESOZOIC or Era of Reptiles	Cretaceous Period		135 million years ago	Lands generally were low, climates were mild, and bird-hipped dinosaurs were abundant and varied. Seas spread widely; ammonoids, belemnoids, and relatives of oysters were common, as were marine reptiles.
	Jurassic Period		180 million years ago	Lands were low; seas covered much of Europe; there were deserts, volcanoes, and swampy forests in western North America. Ammonoids, belemnoids, and marine reptiles were common; near the end of the period, lizard-hipped dinosaurs became very large and spread round the world.
	Triassic Period		230 million years ago	Seas covered much of Europe; ammonoids became common. Ichthyosaurs and early plesiosaurs evolved, as did other reptilian groups and mammals. Lizard-hipped dinosaurs became common, but most of them were small.

PALEOZOIC or Era of Ancient Life	Permian Period	280 million years ago	Coal swamps were much reduced; mountains formed in eastern North America; glaciers spread in South Africa. Large amphibians and reptiles lived in swampy lowlands; shark-like fish and early ammonoids were common.
	Pennsylvanian Period *(Carboniferous Periods)*	330 million years ago	Coal was deposited in great swamps; seas spread but did not last long; mountain-building continued in the East and in Europe. Amphibians and reptiles became good-sized and common; crinoids grew much less abundant.
	Mississippian Period *(Carboniferous Periods)*	345 to 355 million years ago	Seas covered much of North America, especially early in this period. Mountain-building in the East. Sea lilies and sea buds (crinoids and blastoids) were very abundant, but brachiopods and trilobites were less so.
	Devonian Period	405 to 410 million years ago	Most of North America was low and flat, seas spread widely though mountains began to rise and forests grew on low deltas. In the Old Red basins of Europe, fish evolved into amphibians as they tried to remain in water.
	Silurian Period	430 million years ago	Europe remained mountainous, but most of North America was low and much of it was under salt water. Marine life was abundant; jawless "fish" continued to evolve; sea scorpions were common in brackish waters.
	Ordovician Period	500 million years ago	Shifting seas covered more than half of North America, but mountains formed in the East and in Europe. Most corals remained small, but brachiopods and trilobites became common and straight cephalopods grew very large.
	Cambrian Period	570 to 620 million years ago	Most of North America was low, after mountain-building in the Great Lakes region at the end of Precambrian times. Marine animals, especially brachiopods and trilobites, became common fossils, but many other groups existed.
PRECAMBRIAN ERAS (Variously divided on the different continents)		Probably more than 3500 million years ago	Many changes in lands and seas; mountain-building in various parts of the world; great volcanic eruptions; formations of important ore deposits; relatively few fossils.

and so on. But no fossil can say that Cambrian rocks are 500 million years old, or Eocene beds a mere 50 million. Such figures must be determined by comparing the quantities of radioactive materials that were originally contained in rocks with others into which they have disintegrated, or "decayed." Since the speed of disintegration is constant for each substance, these studies yield dates such as those used in the following chapters and in our general time scale.

"Radioactive" dates are not precise; some contain probable errors of several million years. Most dates also are not final; new determinations will change and improve them, and so will new ideas as to where dividing lines should be drawn. Qualified experts will deal with these matters—and since specimens, data, and human minds vary, a century may go by before the final figures come in.

Shall we wait? Not if we want to achieve proportion in our view of life's history. This was unnecessary a century ago, when people "knew" that the earth was created on October 22, 4004 B.C., and that all life appeared before the first weekend. Today, however, we need to express geologic time in intelligible terms. We want to tell how much longer one period was than another; how much time fish took to produce four-legged descendants, and whether Ice-age glaciers melted "when the world was young" or only a few thousand years ago. To do any of these things we must translate geologic ages into years. Since they are numbered in thousands, millions, and hundreds or thousands of millions, does it matter too much that the figures we use are averaged and rounded out, and will someday be refined?

4 SHELLS, SEA-MUD, AND MOUNTAINS

WE HAVE AGREED that fossils are remains or traces of things that lived during past geologic times and were buried in rocks of the earth's crust. There the ancient organisms lay until rains, rivers, rock slides, power shovels, or collectors' picks brought them to light again.

Fossils that are merely washed out of the ground soon become worthless; weather damages them as it did the "boulders" that lay around Bone Cabin. Most remains dug up by power shovels meet their fate as surely, and more rapidly, in rock crushers, cement mills, or lime kilns. Only fossils that are collected, saved, and studied with care can tell the story of life through earth's past. The length of that story astounds many people, and so does the part contributed by water-dwelling organisms that did not have backbones. Many were not even animals or plants, though they still appear under those headings in old or conservative books.

The tale told by these fossils began 1600 to 2700 million years ago. Blue-green algae have been reported from rocks of the latter age; algae, bacteria, and perhaps other creatures occur in iron-bearing beds of northern Michigan whose age has been determined as 1600 and 1800 million years. Such fossils are rare for two reasons: because they were not often preserved, and because they are so small that they are easily overlooked. Many have to be enlarged 250 to 325 times before they can be examined.

Things changed during the following ages; by 1,250,000,000 B.C. or so seas contained banks and reefs of red or blue-green algae that built stony masses while they were alive. Some of these "heads" are barely an inch in width, but others are more than 16 feet. Among later algal banks are worm burrows filled with sand, a few things that seem to be lamp-shells, and a jellyfish. Much later—just

Two types of algal "heads," or stromatolites, from Late Precambrian rocks of Glacier National Park, Montana.

before the Cambrian Period began—other jellyfish, worms, and soft corals called sea pens left impressions in South Australian sandstones.

In our time scale, the Precambrian eras end in one simple line. That scale, however, condenses events that were long and complex, and differed on different parts of the earth. At some places sea bottoms became land; in others mountains were built and worn away; in still others sand filled embayments while glaciers covered nearby lands. Our line, in short, represents a series of events that continued through millions of years.

Fossils from Cambrian Seas

During that time several groups of animals developed hard parts that could be petrified. We say this because Early Cambrian seas were inhabited by varied animals that could not have sprung into existence as a new period began. Petrified fossils include stony sponges that built banks as much as 200 feet thick and 400 miles long and small snails that left actual shells as well as trails made while they crawled over mud devouring algae. On other muddy bottoms lived undoubted brachiopods, or lamp-shells, whose English name means nothing until we note that some later types, when divided and turned upside down, were shaped like diminutive Greek lamps. Early Cambrian species were small and thin-shelled, and many anchored themselves to sandy or muddy bottoms by means of fleshy stalks, as their relatives do today. Though brachiopod shells have two parts, or valves, the bodies differ radically from those of "bivalved" clams.

Far more active than brachiopods were creatures whose fossils are often called "petrified butterflies." Most of them were broad, thin animals 1 to 8 inches long, and they were trilobites, not butterflies. We shall examine a few outstanding Cambrian types and their successors in Chapter 5.

So much for Early Cambrian life as we trace it in petrified fossils. The record still is incomplete, for later formations contain organisms whose ancestors must have been evolving since Precambrian times. Besides glass sponges, lamp-shells, and trilobites, one Middle Cambrian deposit contains specialized jellyfish, as well as naked, spiny, and tube-building worms, creatures that probably were sea cucumbers, and some that looked like clams and shrimps but were related to trilobites. With these fossils, collectors also find silky seaweeds and others with broad leaflike blades which are far from being primitive.

After the Cambrian

Ever since fossils first became common, they have recorded events that are repeated over and over again. One of these is the appearance of new organisms: species, families, and larger groups that did not exist before. Some arose through step-by-step changes in well-known ancestors, but others had few if any known forebears. This was true of most Cambrian animals, which had no known relatives among Precambrian fossils.

Many important groups appeared as epochs or periods began. Then came times of expansion, during which new groups produced descendants that differed in appearance and lived in different ways. Many became amazingly well fitted, or adapted, to their surroundings and the things they had to do to live.

Adaptation was one kind of success; variety and abundance were others. Groups that were varied, abundant, and well adapted lived for millions of years, but sooner or later most of these successful creatures declined or became extinct. Either could happen at almost any time, but extinctions were most widespread at the end of epochs or periods, when seas shifted, lands rose or sank, and climates changed greatly. Highly adapted creatures were often the first to die out. Unspecialized forms might linger on or even produce descendants that evolved into different groups.

Now and then, however, unspecialized creatures neither died out nor evolved into new ones. They lived on and on instead, surviving through epochs, periods, and even eras without important change. Those that exist today appear to be so antique that we often call them living fossils.

Two of these events—decline and extinction—took place at the end of Cambrian times. Hordes of established trilobites and brachiopods died out as broad, shallow seas became land. When the Ordovician Period began and new seas spread, they brought hordes of creatures that were characterized by thick, even stony, shells and supports.

No one knows why these structures were developed, for Ordovician seas did not differ much from those of the Cambrian Period. Yet some corals built separate horn-shaped supports for their bodies while others lived in stony colonies. Bryozoans, whose name deceptively means "moss animals," also built colonies that grew to be large and ornate in Late Ordovician seas. Brachiopods became abundant and many kinds developed shells that grew to be very thick or were strengthened by prominent ridges. Snail shells were round, pointed, or flat on one side and deeply convex on the other.

Middle Ordovician seas also sheltered brachiopods whose descendants are the most successful of living fossils. Called *Lingula* (little tongue), they were and still are small, thin-shelled creatures that pushed tough stalks into mud or sand under shallow sea water. While the animals fed, their stalks were extended; when they were disturbed, their stalks contracted and pulled them into the sediment. *Lingula* was most plentiful on shallow, sandy sea bottoms like those on which it lives today. Among the Philippine Islands, these brachiopods are so abundant that storm waves pile them up to heights of 12 to 30 inches along miles of beach. Yet the creatures reproduce in such abundance that their numbers are not permanently diminished. Instead, destruction seems to give new individuals a chance to grow.

Many Ordovician sea-dwellers died out, but the next two periods saw a great increase in shells and supports. Corals built "horns" that were 25 inches long and 3 inches thick; clams developed sturdy shells; starfish protected themselves with plates of the material that makes up limestone. Even one-celled creatures nicknamed "forams" built small, coiled shells which supported and, when necessary, covered their jellylike flesh. Similar shells would settle by trillions on the bottom of a Mississippian sea, forming thick beds of buff or whitish rock. Known commercially as Indiana Limestone, it is often used in the walls of large buildings.

Thick shells, plates, and supports resisted destruction, and therefore had a chance to become fossils. But why are those fossils often so abundant that hundreds or thousands may be collected in an afternoon? Why are many unbroken or even unworn? Finally, why are they now on land although they lived and died in seas?

Our answer to the first question depends on the fact that these fossils lived in shallow seas which spread over regions that were parts of continents, not oceans. In this they resembled the present-day Baltic Sea, North Sea, and Hudson Bay, which now cover 860,000

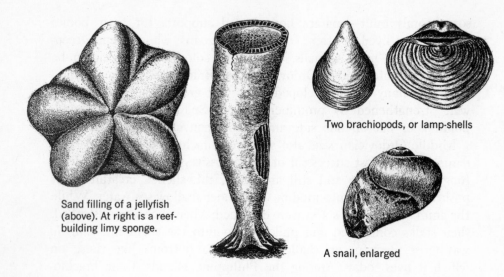

Two brachiopods, or lamp-shells

Sand filling of a jellyfish (above). At right is a reef-building limy sponge.

A snail, enlarged

Some Early Cambrian fossils

square miles of Europe and North America to depths that average 180, 308, and 420 feet. In North America alone, Ordovician seas covered more than 5 million square miles.

Since ancient seas were shallow, they were well lighted, and extensive areas were not very far from shore. This meant that they received minerals from land—and minerals plus sunlight are the basis of abundant sea life. Today it begins with tiny plants that make the water dull green; they are eaten by small animals, and so on up to giant sharks and whales. Similar food chains must have existed in ancient times, though large sharks and whales did not exist before the Cenozoic Era. With whales or without them, however, hordes of fossils exist because ancient seas were good places to live in and provided plenty of food.

Seas that were good to live in also favored preservation of shells and other hard parts without much wear or breakage. It is true that some ancient waters were stormy, with waves that rolled corals over and over and ground shells into bits. In other seas, dead creatures were carried in currents, but so gently that many shells were not deeply worn or broken, and jointed animals were not torn apart. Some seas, finally, were so quiet that mud sank to the bottom and buried its inhabitants where they had lived and died. This is shown

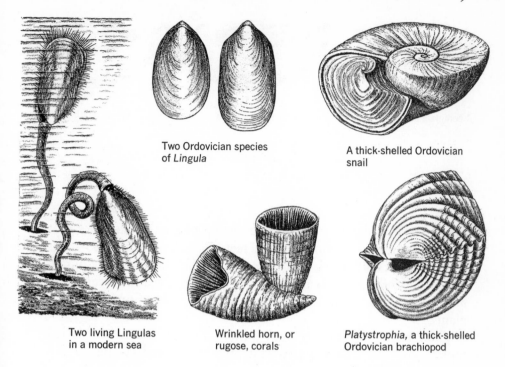

Two Ordovician species
of *Lingula*

A thick-shelled Ordovician
snail

Two living Lingulas
in a modern sea

Wrinkled horn, or
rugose, corals

Platystrophia, a thick-shelled
Ordovician brachiopod

Some typical Ordovician fossils and two modern Lingulas

by bryozoans and corals whose remains still stand upright in shale, and by others that spread in delicate networks over what once was clay. Some fine-grained sandstones contain brachiopods which are crowded together with their tips, or beaks, directed downward and the openings of their shells upward. These plainly are beds or "banks" of fossils which still occupy both the places and positions in which they spent their lives.

From Sea Bottoms to Land

Because many fossils lived, died, and were buried under shallow water, we are tempted to think that a slight shift would raise the beds that contain them and so turn sea bottoms into land. Slight shifts, however, could not put most marine deposits where they are today. As a rule, these rocks accumulated on sea bottoms that sank throughout epochs or periods, and often sank again after new periods

A complete lamp-shell   One part, or valve   An ancient lamp

Why brachiopods are often called lamp-shells

began. As a result, beds settled one on top of another in series that
became hundreds or thousands of feet thick. Some of these series
still lie under salt water. Others come to the surface in mountain
ranges and hills or lie beneath rolling land and plains. Deep wells
have been bored through 2 to almost 8 miles of strata under western
plains.

These rocks have plainly been pushed upward, since they settled
under seas. The task required vast amounts of energy, but it did
not always take the form of earth-shaking, catastrophic upheavals.
Throughout much of North America, marine formations were raised
500 to 5000 feet above sea level so gently and so uniformly that
many show neither bending nor breaking. Others slope no more
steeply than well-engineered roads.

Such rocks also appear in high plateaus like the one that rises both
north and south of Arizona's famous Grand Canyon. They are un-
common in mountains, however, for most strata that make up
peaks have been pushed slantwise, broken into long blocks, or tilted
so much that they dip steeply or appear to stand on edge. Other
beds were squeezed until they arched into folds that would now be
2 to 5 miles high if their crests had not been worn away. In some
places, compression became so great that it broke mountain ranges
80 to 700 miles long and pushed them obliquely upward for distances
of 10 to 30 miles.

Where uplift has been greatest, it has brought rocks from depths
of several thousand feet and has left them in mountains. The tip
of Everest, now 29,028 feet high, consists of sandy marine limestones
that were once covered by later beds.

Few of us can collect on Mount Everest, but it is not hard to find places where fossil-bearing rocks have been raised a mile or more. East of the Silver Gate to Yellowstone Park, for example, U. S. Highway 212 passes Beartooth Lake at an altitude of 8912 feet, and he who climbs Beartooth Butte may find fossils of Cambrian, Ordovician, and Devonian ages. West of Los Alamos, New Mexico, State Highway 4 crosses slopes of marine Mississippian limestone from which brachiopods have been weathered. In Glacier National Park, Montana, a paved highway crosses Logan Pass at 6664 feet, and the parking space at the summit is rimmed by beds of marine Precambrian algae. Other algae are found in a mountain from whose top at least two miles of strata have been removed by erosion. When we raise our binoculars to scan those cliffs, we are likely to see a mountain goat and her kid, climbing to the ledge where they will rest until late afternoon. Though those goats are alpine animals, their resting place is far below the ledge that contains the second algal deposit.

Do we need better evidence that this particular sea bottom has been pushed to a height of more than 3 miles above the depths at which it once lay?

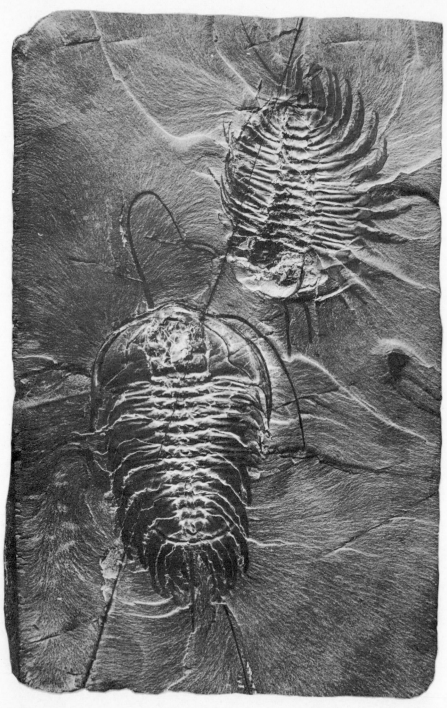

Two Middle Cambrian trilobites, *Olenoides*, from British Columbia. This specimen is in the United States National Museum.

5 SKIN-CRUSTED TRILOBITES

TRILOBITES, AS we know, are sometimes called petrified butterflies; compact species have also been mistaken for stony nuts and toads. Actually, these fossils belong to a class in the phylum of animals with jointed feet, which also includes crabs, lobsters, insects, centipedes, and spiders.

The name trilobite means "three-lobed creature." We readily see that the trilobite body contains three parts which look like head, abdomen, and tail, but the lobes that account for the name run lengthwise and are separated by grooves. Unusually well-preserved fossils also show feelers, or antennae, as well as legs, and eyes that contain many sections, or facets.

Though trilobites were not simple, they were the first animals to leave large numbers of fossils. In many Early Cambrian formations, trilobites are the only fossils that are common and very well preserved.

There are three reasons for this. First, trilobites really were common in many places and at many times. Second, trilobite shells were made of material that was not easily destroyed. Third, the animals shed their shells as they grew and developed new ones, as crabs do today. The number of shells probably varied, but several kinds produced a dozen before they became full-grown. One of these animals might leave a dozen fossils, each showing the entire body at one stage of its development. When shells were broken to pieces, the number of fossils increased with every piece.

Though we usually say that trilobites had shells, *skin-crusts* is a better term. A shell is almost any hard covering: a nut shell, turtle shell, clam shell, and so on. But a nut shell is woody, a turtle shell is bone, and a clam shell consists of hard, limy material. Many trilobite shells became hard, too, but they always began as flexible coats that were built on the surface of the skin. Throughout life they remained thin and flexible where they covered movable joints, and

An Early Cambrian trilobite, *Olenellus*, shedding its skin-crust, which broke open on the cephalon, or "head." The cast-off crust was tough and durable, and readily became a fossil.

the skin readily separated from them when the animals prepared to shed. As its skin-crust split, each trilobite wriggled out and probably hid until its skin was able to build a new and larger crust.

Changes in Trilobites

No one knows when or how trilobites evolved; they apparently did so before skin-crusts grew thick enough to be petrified. One theory says the group began with little, eyeless animals whose descendants added sections as well as organs to their bodies. A more widely held theory, which we shall follow, derives trilobites from jointed sea worms whose bodies contained many sections, or segments, each bearing one pair of legs. As ages passed the segments (also called somites) widened; those that lay just behind the head combined with it and so built up the cephalon, which included both head and forward part of the body. At the rear, other segments combined to form the pygidium, which was much more than a tail. Between these two divisions of the body lay the thorax, which still consisted of segments linked by movable joints, with legs on the underside of each section. Portions of the cephalon and pygidium also retained their legs, though these are seldom preserved in fossils.

Still following this theory, we select five trilobites to show the results of these evolutionary changes. Specimens 1 and 2 are Early Cambrian types called *Olenellus*; the former may closely resemble the creature that first became a trilobite. The pygidium seems to be the original button-shaped end of the body, and the thorax, with its twenty-six sections, suggests a broad, many-jointed worm. The fifteenth segment, however, bears a long spine, and the cephalon has become complex. Its central lobe shows traces of five segments behind the original head.

In one respect Specimen 2 is still more primitive, for its thorax contains forty-four segments instead of twenty-six. But the last twenty-nine segments seem to have shrunk, though the first fourteen have widened and nine of them end in spines. The cephalon also is wide, though only three segments appear behind the original head. If there are more, the grooves that once divided them have vanished.

Specimen 5, the Middle Cambrian *Ogygopsis*, is a combination of contrasts. The whole animal is flattened and broad, its width being two thirds of its length. The thorax contains only eight blunt segments, but five and the head may be traced in the cephalon and at least fourteen appear in the broad pygidium. There is no trace of the long spine seen in *Olenellus*.

These are substantial changes, but they seem trifling when we compare them with others which—if our theory is correct—are shown by Specimens 3 and 4. Though they are fully grown, both fossils measure less than three eighths of an inch in length. Number 3 has three thoracic segments and traces of eight in the pygidium; in 4 the numbers are two and three. In contrast to our first *Olenellus*, this trilobite has lost at least twenty-three segments or has combined them into its pygidium and cephalon. Like Number 3, it also has lost its eyes. As a result, we cannot always tell which end of the little creature is which.

Changes such as these took place again and again in various combinations, for trilobites were a complex class whose members evolved independently through some 390 million years. Long after our fourth fossil had lost most of its segments, one trilobite still possessed eighteen thoracic segments and a two-part pygidium. Several Ordovician and Silurian forms had pygidia that bore no hint of segments— but in Permian times, when trilobites were dying out, one called *Ameura* carried clear traces of eighteen pygidial segments. In one Pennsylvanian species they numbered twenty-six!

Trilobites differed as much in shape, ornamentation, and size as they did in the number of their parts. *Bumastus*, for example, was deep-bodied and smooth, with rounded cephalon and pygidium. Several genera were broad and flattened, with their segments so nearly separate that they suggest clusters of leaves. Other trilobites were small, blunt, and compact, with thick, rough shells, but some tapered to both ends or developed long spines that projected from both cephalon and pygidium. When the thorax also became spiny, the creatures must have resembled animated burrs.

Many spiny trilobites were small, but one was 28 inches long and another, called *Terataspis*, measured 18 to 20 inches. Its crust was dotted with prickers and spikes; its cephalon ended in long spines, as did the segments of its thorax and those that had been combined into the pygidium. Since large spines were set with small ones, the skin-crust provided a prickly mouthful for any creature that attacked *Terataspis*.

How Did They Live?

Trilobites apparently were descended from jointed worms, and many kinds combined wormlike ways with others appropriate to the

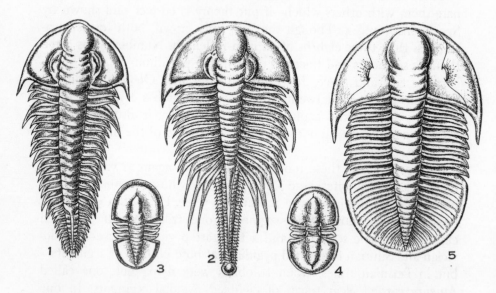

Evolutionary changes in trilobites. Number 1 is a primitive Early Cambrian species of *Olenellus*; 2 is more advanced but still has many sections behind its long spine. Number 5 is a Middle Cambrian species of another genus; it shows that at least fourteen segments have been combined in its pygidium. Numbers 3 and 4 are regarded as highly evolved Middle Cambrian trilobites that have lost most of their segments as well as their eyes.

animals' new status. Primitive types skimmed over the sea bottom by means of their legs, but in swimming the many-jointed bodies also undulated. When crawling became desirable, all trilobites relied on their legs, which often dug into soft mud as they carried their owners forward. Crescent-shaped eyes looked forward, sideways, upward, and a little to the rear, but eyes on stalks were still more versatile. Antennae smelled or tasted food, which often consisted of burrowing worms. *Olenellus* apparently used legs on the underside of the cephalon to dig out worms and push them into the mouth. In spring, female trilobites dug pits and laid eggs in them. Sand then filled the pits and protected the eggs until they hatched and the young ones swam away.

This account is inferential; no human being ever saw a trilobite swim, crawl, dig for food, or excavate a nest for its eggs. But we do know how a trilobite's jointed legs and body could move, fossil trails are fairly common, and irregular pits are just what we should find where the animals dug food from mud or loose sand. Other pits are more regular in form, and their sides bear marks that correspond to the legs and spines of trilobites found in the same strata. These pits also resemble those dug in loose sand by modern horseshoe crabs, which eat worms and are the nearest living relatives of trilobites.

Egg-laying in pits rests on similar evidence. Some hardened fillings are deeper and more precise than those that seem to have been dug for food; markings closely match the spines and cephalons of *Olenellus*. Alternations of mudstone and sand indicate that these pits were dug in the spring, which is the season when horseshoe crabs dig pits for their eggs. May we not infer that trilobites shared, if they did not invent, this instinct?

The thick, bulbous body of *Bumastus* was poorly adapted to swimming or crawling. This trilobite probably plowed through mud, eating worms as it went. Since the eyes were high up on the cephalon, the stirred-up sediment did not blind them.

Getting mud on one's eyes was no problem for trilobites that had lost their eyes as well as most of their body segments. These creatures probably lay or crept slowly on muddy sea bottoms, eating both dead material and little animals that lived in it.

We need not guess at the habits of trilobites with smooth, flattened skin-crusts, pygidia shaped like trenching tools, and eyes on stalks or on top of the cephalon. Fossils sometimes lie just where

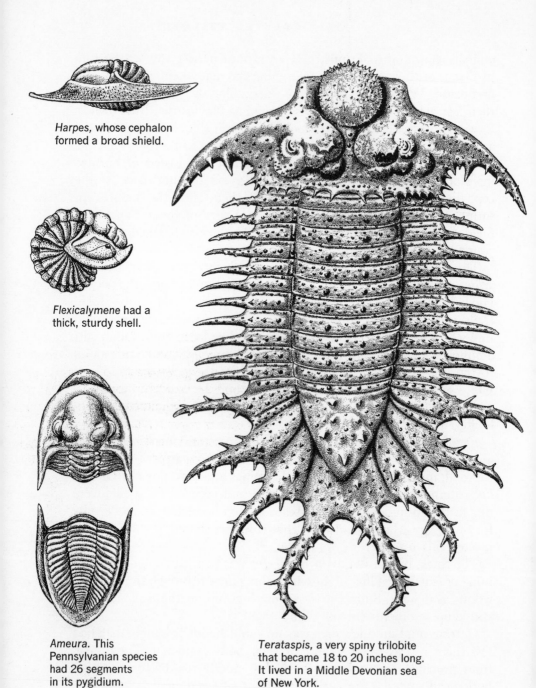

Harpes, whose cephalon formed a broad shield.

Flexicalymene had a thick, sturdy shell.

Ameura. This Pennsylvanian species had 26 segments in its pygidium.

Terataspis, a very spiny trilobite that became 18 to 20 inches long. It lived in a Middle Devonian sea of New York.

Enrolled and spiny trilobites

they lived, with pygidia thrust down into what was a sea bottom and the rest of the body lying upon it. In this position, the animals could eat food that drifted over the mud, but could not be carried away by currents.

Skin-crusts into Armor

We sometimes say that trilobites were supreme in Early Paleozoic seas. That doubtless was true at some times and places; the largest Cambrian animal was a trilobite 18 inches long that weighed about 8 pounds, and a late Ordovician species 30 inches in length was bigger than any of its neighbors. But all trilobites were mild-mannered eaters of plants, carrion, and worms, and they neither fought nor

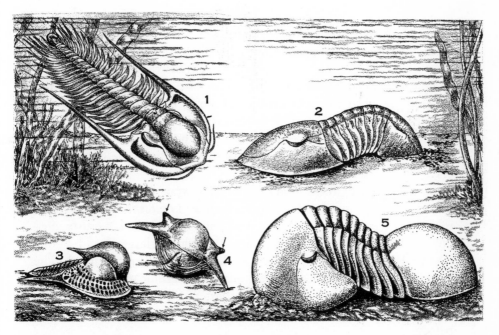

How some trilobites lived. Number 1, *Paradoxides* swimming. Number 2, *Isotelus* lying on the sea bottom with its pygidium thrust into mud. Number 3, *Cryptolithus*, an eyeless creature that crept on mud. Number 4, *Thaleops* enrolled; arrows point to the eyes, which were on stalks. Number 5, *Bumastus* plowing through mud in search of food. These creatures actually lived at different times.

carried weapons. When predators appeared they could only use their skin-crusts as armor.

Terataspis was doubly protected, for his thick, hard crust resisted attack and his spines discouraged efforts to turn him over. Smooth-shelled *Dipleura* folded his shieldlike cephalon against his pygidium and was completely covered; *Calymene* and its relatives built thick skin-crusts that were strengthened by ridges. When these trilobites rolled up tightly they presented surfaces that were difficult to break.

Several trilobites had cephalons that seem much too large for their small bodies. Some crept on sandy bottoms, but others pushed forward with the broad rim of the cephalon just below the surface of loose mud. None of these creatures could roll very tightly, but all were able to tuck the thorax and pygidium under the expanded "head."

Enemies and Extinction

What predators called forth these defenses? Those of Cambrian times have not been discovered, though a few petrified trilobites show that sections had been bitten from their thoraxes. In Chapter 6, however, we shall see that the Ordovician Period brought a host of mollusks with muscular arms and sharp beaks. Ranging from a few inches to 10 or 12 feet in length, these creatures preyed on anything big enough to be worth eating. Though trilobites were less meaty than present-day crabs and lobsters, the new predators found them to be desirable food.

As ages passed, these hungry mollusks were joined by predatory fish. As enemies increased, trilobites such as *Terataspis* covered themselves with spines while types with smooth, thin skin-crusts died out. Then, in Late Devonian times, the whole class entered a long decline that ended in extinction as the Permian Period closed. The last survivors were small animals whose thick armor was strengthened by swellings and ridges. Many of the latter still represented segments that had become part of cephalon and pygidium millions of years before.

6 THE REPETITIVE
HORN-SHELLS

SILURIAN SEAWEEDS swayed as a creature in a coiled shell darted past them. It swam shell-first, with its body and soft, fleshy arms behind, driving itself by jets of water that came from a tube under its head. When the jets stopped, the shell sank beside a trilobite and the arms reached out to seize it.

The trilobite was a half-grown *Bumastus*, plowing its way through mud. As it struggled to dig more deeply, the attacker came part-way out of his shell. His body was smooth, but a hood of rough skin spread above his big eyes. They and the arms made the creature resemble a cuttlefish, squid, or octopus that had backed into the shell of a tightly rolled snail.

The resemblance was natural, for the Silurian predator was related to all these animals. It was also connected, much more closely, with the pearly (or chambered) nautilus. All five are—or were—mollusks belonging to the class of cephalopods. They were given this name, which means "head-foot," because their bodies are so tightly folded that the head and foot are together.

Cephalopods are divided into three subclasses, but only two are characterized by shells large enough to cover the entire body. One of these subclasses is made up of ammonoids, which have been extinct since the end of the Cretaceous Period. The other shell-covered subclass, called nautiloids, includes all cephalopods whose shells are built like the shell of the modern nautilus. Since many members of both subclasses have names that end in *ceras*, which is Greek for "horn," we may give them the English name of horn-shells.

Weatherworn fossils or a modern shell that has been cut in half shows the essential characteristics of nautiloids. The shell is always divided into parts, or chambers, by curved partitions called septa which were built by the rear end of the body. The last chamber is the longest and largest; it also contained the body when the horn-

Some Middle Silurian horn-shells. Number 1 is the species that captured *Bumastus*; 2 is a straight-shelled relative; 3 is an empty, broken shell. It shows part of the living chamber, ten septa, and the siphuncle, as well as nine empty chambers.

shell was alive. A fleshy stalk extended backward through the septa and covered itself with a tube of shelly material. This tube (the siphuncle) is thin in some shells but is thick in others. Thick siphuncles often look like backbones or chains of hollow beads.

Changes in Horn-shells

The horn-shell that caught *Bumastus* was a nautiloid that lived in a sea which covered northern Illinois about 420 million years ago. In spite of its great age, the creature was neither the first member of its subclass nor a primitive one. Nautiloids appeared in Early Cambrian seas, as tiny creatures with straight, cone-shaped shells less than a quarter inch long. As time passed, their descendants grew larger and larger, until some straight horn-shells were 8, 10, or even 12 feet in length. These giants lived in Middle Ordovician seas that extended from New York to Alabama, Kansas, and Saskatchewan.

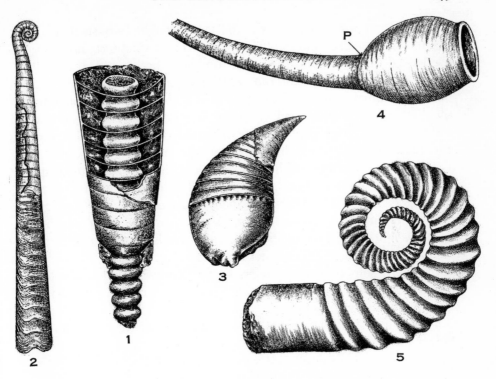

How nautiloids changed. Number 1, part of a cone-shaped species with thin septa and a thick "beaded" siphuncle. Number 2, *Lituites*, which coiled and then became straight; it probably lived in this position. Number 3, a short, curved shell with a large living chamber. Number 4, a slender shell that suddenly became swollen. It soon broke off at P. Number 5, a wrinkled, loosely coiled shell that became smooth and straight during old age.

The living nautilus helps us determine what fossil horn-shells looked like. We already know that the body was short; the round eyes were covered with skin and had slits instead of pupils. The arms could stretch out and pull, but they had no suckers like those on the arms of an octopus. The mouth, which was hidden among the arms, had a beak like a parrot's turned upside down. With that beak, the Silurian hunter bit chunks from the trilobite it had captured.

Some petrified horn-shells preserve stripes and zigzag bands of color which grade from dark above to light below. The animals probably lay on the sea bottom much of the time, or crawled about slowly by means of their arms. When they had to move rapidly, they swam.

Old restorations sometimes showed long, straight horn-shells darting to and fro like underwater missiles. Those pictures, however, overlooked the shells, and they were too big to be ignored. If a shell had been empty except for the stalk of flesh, it would have risen until the animal hung head downward, with only its arms touching the bottom. If it had tried to swim, it would have shot to the surface. Had it attempted to turn, it would have bobbed this way and that, but still would have risen to the surface.

These things would have happened *if*, and they probably *did* happen during Cambrian times. But as straight nautiloids progressed they made changes that kept their shells under control. The simplest change was made again and again, as one nautiloid after another added weight, or ballast, to its shell. Some kinds deposited material around the siphuncle; others thickened the septa, and still others did both. Shells sometimes became so heavy that we wonder whether the creatures could swim. Perhaps they spent most of their time lying on the sea bottom.

Even empty shells would not become unwieldy if they were short. When we make something too long we cut or break off a portion, and some horn-shells developed a similar method. For much of their lives, they built slender shells that were gently curved instead of straight. Then the animals suddenly became larger than they had been, and began to build swollen shells. Just behind each new part was a line of weakness, and there the empty shell broke off.

This was a roundabout method; why not just build a short shell? Though no cephalopod was bright enough to ask that question, many kinds evolved answers to it. Some did so by building very short, wide shells that were straight or gently curved. Then, when the animals were almost ready to stop growing, they narrowed the apertures of their living chambers until they were mere slits or irregular openings. Instead of crawling or swimming, these creatures probably drifted with their shells upright, their bodies downward, and their arms reaching out to find food. The openings were so narrow, however, that they could not pull large victims to their mouths.

Curves and Coils

Early Cambrian nautiloids were straight, but curved shells appeared before the end of the period. There were others in Ordovician and later seas, for curvature apparently evolved several times. Some of

Three contrasting nautiloids. Number 1 had a short shell with a narrow, ir-regular opening. Number 2, a curved shell whose owner crawled on one flattened side of the body, like a snail. Number 3, a species that coiled like a snail but seldom crawled, since its body was small. The color markings on 1 and 2 show plainly in fossils.

these fossils were relatives of shells with narrow or irregular openings, and they probably floated with the body downward. But other curved fossils have wide openings and zigzag color markings that are dark all the way round. These creatures must have kept most of the body outside the shell, using their arms to crawl on one flattened side. They had evolved a new substitute for the flat foot which their ancestors had lost when they became cephalopods.

Tightly coiled horn-shells appeared in Early Ordovician seas, and so did others whose coils were open. Both got long shells into little space. Since the coils were not heavily weighted, they helped keep the animals right-side-up and were not in the way when they swam. Coiled nautiloids survived long after straight ones died out, for the living nautilus is coiled.

Although coiled shells were useful, some nautiloids soon began to uncoil. But they did not merely straighten out, as we straighten a length of hose. Instead, they began by building tightly coiled shells—many, in fact, kept on doing so until they were half or two thirds grown. Some kinds then opened up in loose whorls or abruptly changed to straight living chambers that lost the ridges and frills of earlier stages. Only a few, such as *Lituites*, built small coils and

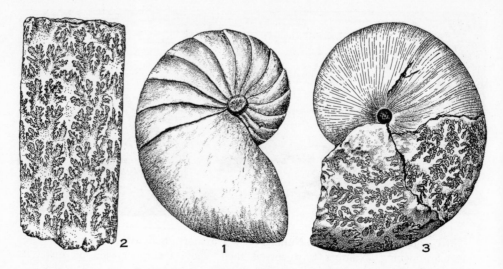

How nautiloids differ from ammonoids. Number 1 is the hardened filling of a nautiloid, showing gently curved sutures. Number 2, straight portion of *Baculites*, with elaborately crumpled septa and sutures. Number 3, a coiled ammonoid with equally elaborate sutures.

followed them with straight, compressed shells that were eight to twelve times longer than the diameters of their coils. Millions of years later, however, other nautiloids coiled in low spires resembling those that had long since been developed by several groups of snails.

Relatives of "Ammon's Stone"

We have traced three types of repetition among ancient cephalopods. In one, nautiloids of several different groups evolved curved shells from straight ones. In the second, other groups of shells straightened after building coils, and in the third, shells that had formed flat coils duplicated the spires of many snails. Another subclass, however, went still further. Besides repeating the shell forms already developed by nautiloids, they evolved some variants of their own whose repetitions involved the septa, not the shape of the shell.

These new horn-shells were the ammonoids, or relatives of *Ammonites*. That mollusk, whose name means "Ammon's stone," supposedly resembled sheep's horns worn by Ammon, foremost of ancient Egyptian gods. Ammonoid bodies were deeply wrinkled

behind and therefore built bent or crumpled septa instead of partitions that curved smoothly like those of nautiloids. This did not
affect the outer surface, but it produced zigzag or very ornate sutures where septa joined the inside of the shell. In their most
elaborate forms, these sutures suggest lace or the complex leaflets
of ferns.

Ammonoids appeared in Middle Devonian seas, when they resembled narrow nautiloids. Long before the Paleozoic Era ended,
however, some descendants of Devonian species built narrow shells
with ridges, or keels, around their edges. Other types became small
and almost ball-shaped or built squat shells with low, broad openings through which the body and arms could extend. Some bizarre
creatures coiled in crude triangles or built triangles for a while and
then finished their lives in bulb-shaped chambers. The sutures of
these odd shells went back to gentle, almost nautiloid curves.

Ammonoids first achieved abundance in Triassic seas. Fossils of
that age include shells of most types we have mentioned, as well as
others with knobs and curved ridges and a few that coiled in taller
spires than those of snail-shaped nautiloids. Sutures, as a rule, were
more deeply crumpled than those of earlier times.

Most Triassic ammonoids died out as that period came to an
end. A few types survived, however, and their descendants became
both abundant and varied during Jurassic and Cretaceous times. With
a few exceptions, they duplicated Triassic and earlier shapes, from
balls to horns and smooth, compressed shells that reached 3 feet in
diameter. Some also developed spiral coils that were higher and much
more slender than any of Triassic age.

We have seen that nautiloids uncoiled at various times and in
varied ways. Some Jurassic ammonoids did so, too, but Cretaceous
species went further and were more bizarre. One extreme was reached
by *Helicoceras*, which ranged through seas that extended from Ten-
nessee to South Dakota, Wyoming, and Texas. *Helicoceras* coiled,
opened and grew in a curve that swung sideways, turned and curved
again, built a spire, and uncoiled once more. *Baculites*, however,
repeated the course taken by *Lituites* during the Ordovician Period;
both coiled for a while and then built slender, straight shells. Since
Baculites was not weighted, it probably crawled or drifted at a slant,
with its coil upward and its arms on the sea bottom, where they
could seize food.

Scaphites and its close relatives had shells that were strengthened by ridges and bumps. Broken specimens often show only coils; complete fossils prove that the shells uncoiled or curved in reverse and then bent so abruptly that the arms must have reached the coils.

To us, such changes in shape seem confusing and wasteful; one theory says they used up so much energy that these ammonoids became extinct. Actually, both *Baculites* and *Scaphites* must have been successful, for they ranged widely and were abundant during the latter half of the Cretaceous Period. When they died out, coiled ammonoids also became extinct. If wasted energy killed *Baculites* and *Scaphites*, what brought extinction to other groups that did not uncoil?

Today, both *Baculites* and *Scaphites* are common fossils. Many

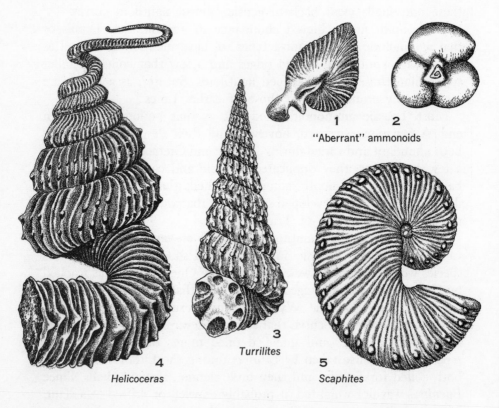

1   2
"Aberrant" ammonoids

4
Helicoceras

3
Turrilites

5
Scaphites

Varied ammonoids. 1 and 2 are coiled in unusual shapes; 3 resembles screw snails; 4 assumes a variety of forms at different stages; 5 is a *Scaphites* that coiled, uncoiled, and bent but died before coiling again.

specimens still preserve their pearly luster; though most shells of *Baculites* are broken, those of *Scaphites* are often complete. Sutures of *Baculites* are so elaborate that chamber fillings interlock and do not fall apart, even when both shell and septa weather away. Such fossils are often mistaken for petrified backbones or snakes.

Baculites had ornate, interlocking sutures, as did many other ammonoids of Jurassic and Cretaceous seas. As Late Cretaceous times began, however, many ammonoids developed septa and sutures which were no more crumpled than those of typical Permian species. Though some shells were curved, more were as tightly coiled as shells whose sutures were more ornate than those of *Baculites*. Simplification of septa and sutures did not demand simplification of shells.

Belemnoids and Squids

We have completed our story of horn-shells, but one tale of repetition is still to be told. It begins with belemnoids, whose fossils usually resemble an old-fashioned wooden pen holder with a deep pit at the large end. The pit once held a small conical shell containing several septa and chambers.

This chambered shell tells us that belemnoids were descended from small, straight nautiloids. As we learned in Chapter 2, however,

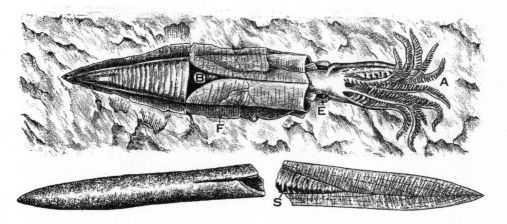

A fossil belemnoid showing eyes (E), arms (A), ink bag (B), and parts of the fins (F). Below this fossil are two guards. One, which is split lengthwise, shows part of the conical shell (S).

the living belemnoid was a torpedo-shaped animal whose body completely covered its hard parts. It had large round eyes, balancing fins that spread sideways, and ten fleshy arms. Two of the arms seem to have borne sucking disks that probably caught fish; the other eight arms carried paired rows of hooks that clung to soft or slippery victims.

The rocks in which fossil belemnoids are found show that the animals swam in shallow, near-shore waters as well as in open seas. The creatures appeared during Mississippian times, reached their greatest abundance during the Cretaceous Period, and died out in the Eocene Epoch. Their role as active molluscan hunters was taken over by squids.

Squids may be descendants of early belemnoids; if so, they have lost all except a trace of their ancestors' shell and "pen." In spite of this, most species are torpedo-shaped swimmers with goggle eyes, balancing fins, and ten arms. In short, though they have changed so much that their ancestry is doubtful, squids resemble belemnoids in shape, speed, method of swimming and catching food, and the habit of swimming in "schools" that often range far from shore. Like belemnoids, squids defend themselves by ejecting inky liquid that paralyzes pursuers' smelling organs. Predaceous fish that have been "shot" by this liquid do not recognize squids even when they touch the mollusks.

7 STALKS, STARS, AND DOLLARS

BURLINGTON, IOWA, began as a trading post on the Mississippi River. Today the city spreads over nearby hills, and its factories turn out products that range from steam turbines to electronic equipment. To fossil hunters, however, Burlington's hills are famous for the crinoids that were collected from them during the late 1800s.

Here we encounter a note which, for today's collector, becomes a discouraging refrain. Most of those crinoids were found between 1860 and 1890; fine corals were abundant beside the Ohio River during the 1870s and 80s; trilobites were scattered over a Cincinnati hillside 80 years ago but are not to be picked up today. Why are they no longer available? Why do collecting localities, like their fossils, often belong to the past?

There are many answers to these questions, but they boil down to three. The first reminds us that fossils often occur in "pockets" which formed where the organisms grew or where their remains were left by streams, waves, or currents in the sea. A small crinoid bank is such a pocket; so is the shale containing carbonized Middle Cambrian fossils, some of which are illustrated in Chapter 2. If a pocket is small it can be "worked out"; once its fossils have been collected, no more are to be found.

Our next answer is the second half of an apparent contradiction. Rain and frost, as we know, can destroy fossils; they turn corals into pebbles, break shells to bits, and reduce massive bones to boulders like those Walter Granger found at Bone Cabin. On the other hand, many invertebrates must be weathered out of rock before they can be seen, collected, and studied. Weathering is rapid in clays and soft shales, from which new supplies of fossils may appear every spring or after heavy rains. Hard limestone, however, crumbles very slowly; the crinoids collected at Burlington between 1860 and 1890 had been freed by a hundred centuries of crumbling and wear. Good collecting ended when those fossils were removed. Ten thousand years from now, specimens may become plentiful again. Meanwhile, fossil hunters who want good crinoids have to look elsewhere for them.

Finally, the spread of cities has destroyed many collecting localities, and others have succumbed to technologic changes. In Cincinnati, university buildings cover a hill where collectors once went every spring to hunt tightly rolled trilobites. The banks of Big Creek, near Cleveland, once were a source of fossil fish; during the 1920s Big Creek Basin was taken over by suburban streets, houses, and lawns. Limestone hills of Burlington have also been covered by the city that once was a trading post.

Many clay pits and quarries still operate as actively as they did long ago. But mechanical diggers do not stop to let workmen pick up fossils, and rock crushers destroy crinoids or corals as readily as they break up limestone. On the other hand, German quarries where workmen once found jellyfish, horseshoe crabs, insects, and even reptiles now stand idle because coated metal plates do work that once required slabs of pure and evenly bedded limestone. The year-in-year-out demand for fossils is not great enough to keep quarries in operation.

Still, civilization is not wholly bad for the collector. Paved roads

Limestone made up largely of broken crinoid stalks (left), and a cystoid with stalk and two arms (right). The limestone was found at Burlington, Iowa.

reach localities once inaccessible, and Jeeps go where wheel-tracks stop. Road cuts often expose fossil-bearing strata, and drills that sink oil wells bring specimens—always small ones—from rocks hundreds or thousands of feet below the surface. Acids and other chemicals are used to remove delicate specimens from rock, and X-ray machines photograph fossils while they are still covered by stone. For fossils such as crinoids, however, nothing quite equals a specimen that is weathered out of limestone, with only small bits of rock still to be removed.

Animals on Stalks

Crinoids are often called sea lilies because their cuplike or lily-shaped bodies are usually borne upon stalks. There the resemblance ends, however, for lilies are plants that live on land and crinoids are marine animals related to sea urchins and starfish. All belong to the phylum of echinoderms: animals characterized by hard plates and spines that form *in* the skin but never *upon* it, like a trilobite's crust or a nautiloid's shell. The plates and spines also consist of calcite, which is the principal mineral in limestone. As much as 85 per cent of the limestone at Burlington consists of crinoids themselves and of calcite from their plates and spines.

Echinoderms are often divided into two great groups: those with stalks and those without them. The former, however, began as small creatures shaped like eggs or flattened balls which fastened themselves directly to dead shells or lay upon hard-packed mud. Plates in the skin were many and small, and the mouth opened on the upper surface of the body. A less attractive and imposing ancestor can hardly be imagined.

Ancestors need not be imposing, however; what they require is the ability to survive through thousands or millions of years plus a tendency to produce changed offspring that can live, reproduce, and repeat that process. In these respects the simple echinoderms excelled, for their direct descendants included eleven of the twelve echinoderm classes, some with stalks and others without. Three of the stalked groups became so abundant that they demand our attention here.

This statement must be qualified; some cystoids remained stemless, had many small plates on their bodies, and probably looked like the first "spiny skins." Others, however, developed cup-shaped bodies that were covered with large plates and were supported on

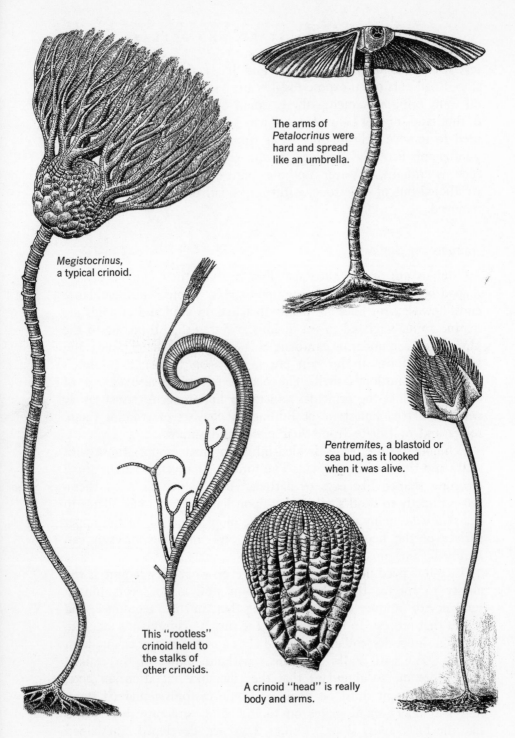

Megistocrinus,
a typical crinoid.

The arms of
Petalocrinus were
hard and spread
like an umbrella.

Pentremites, a blastoid or
sea bud, as it looked
when it was alive.

This "rootless"
crinoid held to
the stalks of
other crinoids.

A crinoid "head" is really
body and arms.

Four varied crinoids and a blastoid, or sea bud

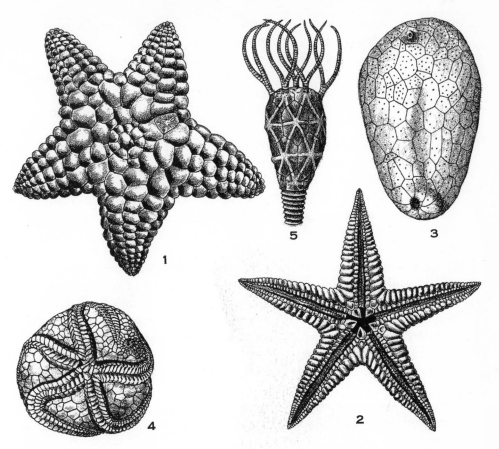

Primitive and advanced echinoderms. Number 1, *Hudsonaster*, an Ordovician starfish. Number 2, undersurface of *Devonaster*, showing opening for the mouth and the grooves that contained tube feet. Number 3, a primitive Ordovician cystoid. Number 4, an edrioaster that was attached to a shell. Number 5, a "dawn crinoid" of Cambrian age.

stalks made of round sections. Jointed arms with small branches waved to and fro, gathering food and sending it to the mouth.

Blastoids are often called petrified nuts; since their technical name means "budlike," the term "sea buds" is a substitute. In life, blastoids probably looked like small, shaggy flowers, for great numbers of tiny arms extended from the body. It was covered by five thick V-shaped plates which almost enclosed the broad, cross-ridged areas where food collected by the arms was taken to the mouth. Small plates that covered those areas and the mouth (which was on top of the body) are almost always missing from fossils.

Most blastoids lived in colonies under shallow, quiet seas. Their jointed stalks broke to pieces soon after death, but their bodies frequently remained intact and collected in low spots. Great numbers are sometimes found in pockets of weathered Mississippian limestone.

If blastoid colonies suggest submarine flower beds, crinoids imply whole gardens. Although they began on a small scale in Ordovician seas, they prospered during the Silurian, Devonian, and Mississippian Periods, and again in the Permian. Mississippian crinoid banks must have covered acres of sea bottom. If living species are reliable guides, colors ranged from whitish to yellow, pink, red, lavender, and deep blue.

Eight hundred species of crinoids are living today, and many of them are abundant. Since they live in water 600 to 15,000 feet deep, however, they are among the least familiar of the ocean's inhabitants.

Crinoids may have dwelt in depths for ages, or they may have retreated to deep, dark, cold waters within the last 50 or 60 million years. The latter theory is suggested by the fact that many modern crinoids have become very different from any that lived in ancient seas which spread over continents. The group called feather stars even lose their stalks as they grow, swim at depths of 3500 to 4500 feet, and sometimes rise to the surface and rest among rocks near shore.

Feather stars are interesting, but they are not typical. As a typical crinoid we may choose *Megistocrinus evansi*, from Mississippian beds at Burlington. Its cup-shaped body was covered with thick plates; the arms branched several times; each branch once bore many delicate branchlets that are sometimes preserved in fossils. The jointed stalk divided into rootlike structures that grew over and even into the mud. They anchored *Megistocrinus* to the sea bottom but—unlike the roots of plants—they did not soak up water or mineral matter.

Megistocrinus was a typical crinoid, but there were many variations from its basic plan. Some crinoids developed deep, vase-shaped bodies; others became so small that we wonder how they managed to build stalks and arms. Some arms were reduced to mere stubs, a few expanded like sheets of chain mail, and others looked like jointed claws or spread into small, stony umbrellas. Stalks grew long or shortened into mere stubs; roots became plated bulbs or massive anchors; some disappeared from crinoids that clung to other things by means of branches from the stalks. One crinoid lost both roots and stalk, but was buoyed up by its long, feathery arms. Vast schools of these creatures drifted in Late Cretaceous seas that extended from Kansas to western Wyoming. Their fossils literally fill thin layers of limestone.

Starfish and Sea Urchins

Stalked echinoderms kept their mouths directed upward, even when they lost their stalks. Stalkless starfish and their kin reversed that position, and so did sea urchins.

Starfish apparently began when a Cambrian animal that was shaped like a flattened ball rolled over and began to eat things that lay or crept on the mud. In time the ball began to bulge in five places, along the grooves that gathered food. When the Ordovician Period began, descendants of these bulging balls had become animals shaped like plump versions of our conventional star. Since Middle Ordovician times, typical starfish have had five or more pointed rays, each containing a branch of the stomach and other internal organs. The mouth still opens at the center of the undersurface, there is no front or rear to the body, and the animal crawls with fleshy tube "feet" that extend from the underside of the rays. Long tubes at the tip of each ray feel for food or taste it in the sea water.

Starfish feed in several ways, but only one is shown by fossils. These particular animals crawled onto clams, took hold of the shells

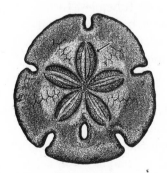

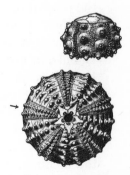

Keyhole urchin   Heart urchin   Symmetrical urchin

(Arrows point to ambulacra)

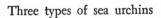

Three types of sea urchins

Clypeaster aegypticus, a very thick-shelled sea urchin. Its spines were short and thin.

with their tube feet, and pulled. As they did so, the starfish secreted a liquid which made the clams relax. When their shells opened, starfish stomachs flowed over them and digested their flesh. Ordinarily, the meal was completed and the starfish crawled away. But when mud or sand settled quickly and deeply, the hungry animals were buried while they lay on the shells of their prey.

The starfish body is flexible, but the shell of plates that covers a typical sea urchin is not. It is a rigid and sometimes very thick structure that keeps its maker in one definite shape.

Some early sea urchins resembled cantaloupes in form; others had the proportions of doorknobs but were covered with tubercles. In fossils these seem ornamental; during life, they were bases for the attachment of spines that ranged from long, slender needles to thick clublike or even bottle-shaped structures. In some forms, the tips of the spines spread so broadly that they must have fitted together in a second coat around the shell.

All sea urchins show five double rows of plates containing holes through which tube feet now extend. These ambulacra correspond to the grooves on the underside of a starfish, though they show best on the urchin's upper surface and may not extend beyond it. The sea urchin's mouth, like that of the starfish, is on its underside.

Many sea urchins had—and still have—shells in which the ambulacra are alike in size and position, dividing the shell into equal parts. In other shells, one ambulacrum extends forward and the others are arranged in pairs on either side. The former group are the urchins that have long spines or thick ones; modern hatpin urchins use them to repel possible attackers. The animal's skin is sensitive to light and shade; when a shadow falls upon an urchin, it promptly turns its spines in that direction. We may assume that ancient long-spined urchins shared this habit and had spines that caused stinging pain.

Sea urchins with right and left sides have short spines that often look like hair. The shells, however, may be large and thick, with internal plates and bars that give extra strength. That is especially true of the cake urchins, which range from 3 to 7 inches in length, and whose ambulacra look like petals. These big urchins are common and very attractive fossils in Tertiary rocks of North America, though some of the finest specimens come from the vicinity of Cairo, Egypt.

Sand dollars are very thin sea urchins whose shells are almost flat on the underside. They, too, are strengthened by rods and plates, which leave very little space for the internal organs. Especially thin species are pierced by narrow holes. Sand dollars crawl on sand or in it. Most of the living species are found near the coasts of North America and Japan. Fossils are commonest in Cenozoic deposits near the Pacific coast, though they also are found in the South and East. One Ice-age, or Pleistocene, species is still the commonest living sand dollar from Mexico to Alaska.

Fossil and a restoration of a bone-covered ostracoderm. This primitive fishlike creature lived near the mouth of a Devonian river in what now is Wyoming. Princeton University.

8 FROM FINS TO LEGS AND LAND

WHILE TRILOBITES crawled and horn-shells caught them, important events took place in fresh waters and on adjacent lands. Though these events brought death to uncounted creatures, they finally led to the evolution of four-legged animals that could live on land.

No one knows just where this change took place, but its site may have been a land that included northern Europe and apparently stretched westward to Greenland. Some books call it the Continent of the Old Red Sandstone after its most famous formation. The "Old Red" actually is a series of sandstones, conglomerates, marls, and lavas that accumulated throughout most of the Devonian Period. On the time scale we are using, its oldest beds settled some 400 million years ago, and its youngest no less than 350 million.

The Old Red Continent was a land of high, rugged mountain ranges separated by valleys or basins into which lavas sometimes poured from fissures as well as volcanoes. The climate was warm to tropical; dry seasons alternated with wet ones in which cloudbursts turned dried-up streams into torrents and filled valleys with shallow lakes. Water-dwellers prospered while the rains lasted but died by millions when drouth reduced rivers and lakes to foul pools and expanses of sun-baked sand and mud.

In spite of these rigorous conditions, both fish and fishlike creatures were common. The latter belonged to the group called agnaths, whose name—it means "jawless ones"—describes their simple, slitlike mouths. *Cephalaspis*, one of the best-known agnaths of Old Red times, had a solid, bony shield on the head and a flexible coat of plates and scales that extended to the tip of the tail. The head-shield covered a bony skull which contained eyes, brain, nerves, and gills that breathed oxygen from water. The rest of the skeleton consisted of cartilage, or gristle, which vanished soon after the creature died. The tail bore a fin and so did the back, but two finlike structures behind the head seem to have been mere flaps of flesh covered by skin and scales. Paired fins and jaws apparently came into existence when agnaths evolved into fish.

That took place before Devonian times, for fish of several types were common in Old Red lakes and streams. Some were small, spiny creatures; others resembled armored agnaths but had one pair of stiff, bone-covered fins. Still others were normally fish-shaped creatures with bones inside their bodies as well as protective plates and scales.

These ancient fish also had gills, as do their modern relatives. Those gills, however, were not too important, for many Old Red fish had lungs and used them to breathe oxygen from air, not from water. By this means, members of two groups lived through dry seasons during which other fish and agnaths died.

One of these groups was made up of "true" lungfish, by which we mean creatures like those to which the name is given today. The nearest relatives of Old Red lungfish now live in parts of Australia where drouths still occur every year. Even when water is plentiful, however, Australian lungfish swim to the surface, stick out their

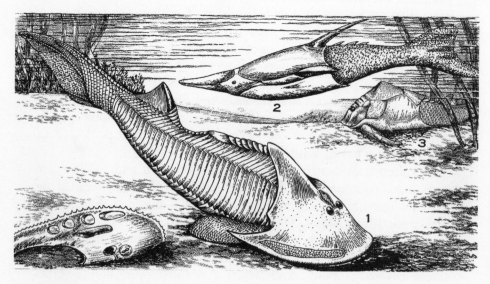

Number 1, *Cephalaspis* and 2, *Pteraspis*, two armored agnaths of the Old Red Sandstone. Number 3 is an armored fish from the same formation.

snouts, and take in air. Lungfish of the Old Red probably shared this habit, and they surely inhaled air when ponds and streams became shallow and lost oxygen through the decay of dead fish and plants. Perhaps the creatures could even survive for a while in mud, as their living relatives do when water disappears.

Lungfish, however, were too highly specialized *as lungfish* to get away from water and mud, even briefly. Lungfish also were unable to produce descendants that would be creatures of any other sort. These changes could only be made by fish that breathed air and had three other qualifications which no true lungfish possessed.

First of these qualifications was a primitive set of bones in skull, jaw, and skeleton. Lungfish had developed too many skull bones and then had turned part of them into cartilage. Some bones in the jaw, as well as the skeleton, had also become cartilaginous.

Second among essential qualifications was a set of pointed teeth.

A lungfish's tooth

Lungfish and fringe-fin. Number 1, *Dipterus*, a primitive lungfish rising to the surface to breathe air. Number 2, one tooth of *Dipterus*. Number 3, *Osteolepis*, an active predaceous fringe-fin of the Old Red Sandstone.

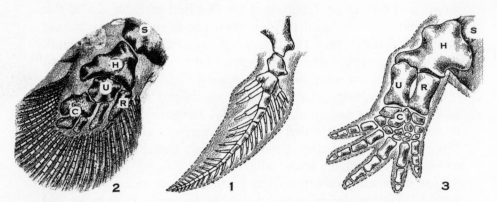

Number 1, bones in the long, flexible fin of a lungfish. Numbers 2–3, bones in the fin of a fringe-finned fish and an amphibian. Letters indicate identical bones in a forefin of the former and foreleg of the latter.

Lungfish had lost the teeth from their jaws; those that remained on the roof of the mouth were broad plates fit only to crush hard-shelled food.

Third came fins with short, sturdy basal lobes containing muscles and bones that could—and would—become the framework of legs and feet. The rest of the fin was a fringe of small bones connected by skin. It could—and would—disappear. The lungfish fin was long, flexible, and leaflike, with soft "bones" that could not have turned into the skeleton of a leg.

Professor Alfred S. Romer of Harvard has outlined the steps by which fringe-finned fish and some of their descendants became four-legged animals. When drouth shrank streams and lakes into pools, both fringe-fins and lungfish took refuge in them. For a while they got along equally well, but when pools became mudholes only fringe-fins could struggle out by means of their fin-lobes and creep across low ground in a frantic effort to find other pools. Those that did so plunged into water and lived; if they possessed especially long, muscular fin-lobes, they also had a chance to pass that character on to their offspring.

Here we pause to make a clear distinction between what those fringe-finned fish were trying to do and the ultimate result of their efforts. The fish *were not* trying to live on land, nor were they making an effort to turn their fins into legs. They *were* blindly leaving places where there was no water, and were equally blindly going to-

A Devonian fringe-finned fish begins to crawl overland to find water. In the distance, a fish that cannot crawl struggles on mud before dying.

ward places where a little water remained. Those that found such pools went no farther unless the pool was already overcrowded, or unless it, too, became dry. If it did, refugees repeated their struggle to find more water in which they could and would remain fish.

We add those words "and would" for good reason, since no fish big enough to make its way to water ever developed legs. But as millions of dry and then wet seasons passed, some fish whose fin-lobes had taken them to water produced offspring whose lobes were longer, with sturdier muscles and bones. When these offspring also lived through drouths, the process was repeated. In time it produced a new sort of creature that had lost its fin fringes, but whose lobes had grown into legs and feet with toes.

We have traced this one series of changes, but they did not take place alone. With them came modifications in size, skull, and skeleton—modifications which added up to a new class of animals, which we call amphibians. Their modern representatives include newts, salamanders, frogs, and toads.

Some theorists have pictured early amphibians as creatures that strove to spend their whole lives on land. For 40 million years, however, they were defeated by soft eggs that had to develop in water, and by young that could breathe only with plume-shaped gills like those of a newly hatched fringe-fin. But at last some unwittingly cre-

Ichthyostega, a primitive amphibian with legs and feet but a fishlike fin on its tail. This creature lived in Greenland about 345 million years ago.

ative female did away with these obstacles. She laid eggs that would hatch into young whose lungs could be used at once. She also wrapped those eggs in membranes filled with liquid that took the place of water and covered them with tough shells. Thus equipped, her progeny became reptiles and truly terrestrial quadrupeds.

This story is direct and dramatic; it also seems to be untrue. The oldest known amphibian gives no hint of being a thwarted land-dweller; it is a fish-shaped creature about 4 feet long that had awkward, sprawling legs and a tail with fins. If these structures mean anything, they tell us that the animal swam happily through lakes and rivers in what is now Greenland and went ashore only when he had to do so. Perhaps he, too, was beset by dry seasons that turned his home waters into mud.

That, however, is supposition; we know little about the climate of Greenland in Late Devonian and Early Mississippian times. But we do know that while amphibians supposedly strove to become land-dwellers, most of those that are known actually evolved into aquatic swimmers. We know, too, that most reptiles, when they appeared, also spent their adult lives in streams, lakes, and swamps.

Does that seem strange? Not when we consider the evidence furnished by fossils. Fringe-finned fish were aquatic carnivores that fed on other fish. Early amphibians were carnivorous, too; besides fish,

Seymouria, a link between amphibians and reptiles that lived in Texas during Early Permian times. At the right is a petrified reptilian egg, also of Permian age.

their diet soon included other amphibians. The first reptiles also seem to have been meat-eaters, yet Early Pennsylvanian forests were inhabited only by millipedes, spiders, insects, and a few small amphibians. What could reptiles do except live in the water and feed on fish, amphibians, and smaller or more sluggish reptiles?

But why should any water-dweller lay eggs that could develop on land and hatch into lung-breathing young ones?

Again Professor Romer offers a plausible theory. As soon as amphibians began they prospered; in 30 million years or so, they and fish must have made great demands on available supplies of food. Moreover, eggs laid in water were likely to be eaten, and so were tadpoles that might hatch from them. There also remained the threat of dry seasons, even though they were not as severe as they had been during Old Red times. Any vertebrate which laid eggs that could develop on land freed both eggs and newly hatched young from these dangers.

If Romer is right, egg-laying on land became established because it gave this selective advantage over egg-laying in water. When a few young ones began to stay on land, they too profited by freedom from hungry neighbors. Once some reptiles established themselves on land, others were able to prey upon them, and so the cycle progressed. Long before the Pennsylvanian Period, or Coal Age, ended there were reptiles 5 to 8 feet long that could not have lived in water if they had wanted to do so.

These creatures were highly specialized, but one "missing link" between amphibians and reptiles lived on through millions of years into the Permian Period. Its remains were buried in red shaly deposits of north-central Texas, and have been named *Seymouria* for the county seat near which they were found.

Some experts call *Seymouria* a very primitive reptile; others say he remained an amphibian. In either case, he was a short-legged, stocky, ugly quadruped about 20 inches in length. His skull was broad and flat on top, with bones essentially like those of more ancient aquatic amphibians. The short, thick legs sprawled sideways; the backbone was heavy and stiff; the tail, which was thick near its base, tapered abruptly to a point. The whole body was hardly built for swimming, but if *Seymouria* lived on land he crawled with his belly flat on the ground. Restorations usually show the male among simple ferns, while his mate rests sleepily near some tough-shelled, elongate eggs that are partly covered with sand. They imply that the creatures were reptiles. If *Seymouria* still belonged among amphibians, the eggs should be soft and covered with water.

9 LIFE AND DEATH
ON DELTAS

WHILE FRINGED fins evolved into legs and amphibians produced reptiles, great changes took place on the earth. Shallow seas spread widely and then turned into land; land crumpled into mountains, and newly filled basins became swamps in which coal accumulated.

We should say that the *materials* of coal accumulated, for the stuff that settled in those swamps was dead trunks, stems, and leaves, mixed with fine mud and other sediment. As the dead plants settled, they slowly decayed into mucky peat and then into lignite, which was compressed into coal under the weight of rocks that settled on top of it. This part of the process usually took millions of years.

Coal swamps once were pictured as hot, steamy morasses where any animal that did not swim slithered over bottomless mud. This picture does not exaggerate the humidity, but the climate apparently was warm rather than intensely hot. It also was uniform, with little change from season to season or from one part of the world to another. This, in turn, allowed the same or very similar plants to grow from subpolar to equatorial regions and on every continent.

The largest of those plants were scale trees, which reached diameters of 4 to 6 feet and were 60 to 100 feet high. Leaves like broad, oversized pine needles grew directly from their trunks and branches. When the leaves fell off they left scars that still look like scales, thus giving the trees their everyday name. The only living relatives of scale trees are so-called ground pines and ground cedars, which creep under forests.

Vines clung to the trunks of scale trees, and ferns grew in their shade. Some kinds had leaves 6 feet long; others developed thick, woody stems 30 to 50 feet high. True ferns, however, were outnumbered by seed ferns, which had nutlike seeds at the tips of their leaves.

Some typical plants of a coal swamp. Number 1, several species of *Lepidodendron*, and 2, *Sigillaria*, both scale trees related to modern club mosses. Number 3, tree fern. Number 4, *Cordaites*, related to conifers. Number 5, several species of *Calamites*, which were ancient scouring rushes.

Horsetails, or scouring rushes, are now small plants that live on either moist or dry, sunny ground. Horsetails of the coal swamps grew in wet places or even in very shallow water, reached heights of 30 feet and diameters of 12 to 14 inches. In many places they formed canebrakes much more dense than the canebrakes of our present-day South.

Both amphibians and reptiles swam in coal swamps, and the reptiles crept into forests when the time came to lay eggs. As we have seen, this led to life on land and to the development of purely terrestrial creatures 4 to 8 feet in length that weighed 50 to 150 pounds.

In Europe, the time of great coal swamps is called the Late Carboniferous or Coal Age and ranks as an epoch, not as a period. In America, the Coal Age is usually called the Pennsylvanian Period, though it may be bracketed with the Mississippian as the Carboniferous Periods. We have done this in Chapter 3.

Red Beds and Amphibians

It is often supposed that geologic periods end in upheavals, eruptions, and other catastrophes. Such events did close the Pennsylvanian, or Late Carboniferous, in Europe and Asia. In much of North America, however, seas merely grew shallow and disappeared. In the West, this was followed by sinking that let a new sea spread from central Texas to Nebraska and eastward to Ohio. In Kansas it became so salty that little or nothing could live in it and rock salt settled on its bottom. In northern Texas, however, sea water was replaced by new Permian land.

That word "new" is appropriate, for this land was a complex series of deltas built by rivers that brought mud from mountains to the east and south, and deposited it in dark red beds. Though some nearby regions had long dry seasons, deltas on which the Red Beds settled were crisscrossed by rivers that kept lowland forests moist and often spread into swamps. They allowed both amphibians and reptiles to live in water, on land, or in the damp zone between them.

Permian amphibians ranged from small mud-grubbers to big, predatory carnivores. Chief among the latter was *Eryops*, a plump, broad-bodied creature with short, massive legs, a strong swimming tail, and an over-all length of 5 to 7 feet. His skull was bony, rough, and massive; his jaws were set with sharp, conical teeth, and others

Eryops (above) was a Permian amphibian 5 to 7 feet long. On the bottom are three individuals of bony-headed *Diplocaulus*.

grew from the roof of the mouth. *Eryops* probably fed largely on fish, which were common in swamps and streams of the deltas. His shape suggests that he also sunned himself on mudbanks, as alligators do today. *Eryops* must have stayed very close to the water, however, for he could not raise his body off the ground and run, as alligators and crocodiles do.

Small amphibians were more active but less dangerous. Sixteen-inch *Cacops* apparently crawled on land, though the ridge of bone along his back must have made him stiff and awkward. Other amphibians were common in the region that is now northeastern Arizona. There beds of buff sandstone contain great numbers of footprints, many of which were made by creatures not much larger than *Cacops*.

Diplocaulus, of the Texas deltas, probably never went on land. This bizarre amphibian possessed a narrow, flattened body, a long

Varanosaurus (1) and *Diadectes* (2), two reptiles of the Permian deltas. Number 3 is the stiff-backed amphibian *Cacops*.

swimming tail, and short, weak legs that must have been useless. The head, however, was a wide triangle of massive bone, with the mouth on the underside. *Diplocaulus* apparently grubbed for worm-like creatures that crawled on the bottoms of streams and swamps. Between meals the amphibian lay on mud in a state of near-unconsciousness that was deeper and lasted longer than sleep. The giant salamander of modern Japan spends most of its life in a similar state.

Reptiles of the Deltas

Land-dwelling reptiles seem to have begun with creatures much like *Seymouria* that lived in Middle Pennsylvanian forests. *Seymouria* itself was an inhabitant of the Red-bed deltas, as were many reptiles that neither looked nor acted like amphibians. One reptile that has been found in Oklahoma was 12 feet long and weighed about 730 pounds.

Meat-eaters of the deltas were more varied than herbivorous reptiles. One of the former was named *Varanosaurus* because it resembled modern monitor lizards, whose technical name is *Varanus*. Although *Varanosaurus* undoubtedly was a hunter, his hind legs could hardly lift his body from the ground. He must have lain in wait for prey, which he captured in short, scrambling attacks.

The largest meat-eaters of the deltas are called *Dimetrodon*. There were several species of these reptiles, and some of them lived in Texas before the Pennsylvanian Period closed. They departed as the Early Permian sea spread eastward; when it gave way to swamps their descendants returned in the form of new species 9 to 11 feet long that weighed as much as 670 pounds. Their name refers to teeth of two lengths; daggerlike stabbers at the front of the mouth and shorter cutting teeth along the sides.

Dimetrodon has been nicknamed the "tiger of the deltas." Like the tiger, he hid until his prey came near, but the jungles in which *Dimetrodon* waited consisted of horsetails, not grasses, and he rushed to the attack on the ground, not by leaping upon his victim. The ancient reptile also killed with his stabbing teeth, for he could not strike with his forelegs and feet.

Two kinds of teeth were *Dimetrodon's* most significant possession, but his "fin" was the most puzzling. We are careful to put the word "fin" in quotes, for the structure actually was a web of skin stretched over tall, slender spines that grew upward from the back. On a reptile 11 feet long, the spines were as much as 4 feet high. Fossils show that many spines were broken. Some seem to have healed promptly, but others became diseased.

We can only guess how this dry-land, immovable fin was used. Some old books show *Dimetrodon* upside-down with the fin in water, where it served as a keel. Other books show only the spines, which supposedly looked like horsetail stems and so helped the big reptile hide in thickets. Another theory suggests that *Dimetrodon* used the fin to warm himself by sitting broadside to the sun on cool mornings. During hot afternoons, he could rest in the shade and use the fin as a radiator to get rid of heat if he had become too warm. Overheating is dangerous to reptiles, and *Dimetrodon* was too big to snuggle down among cool, dead leaves on the floor of the forest, as some tropical snakes do today.

The so-called fin was not found in *Dimetrodon* alone; it was developed and elaborated by a neighbor, *Edaphosaurus*. His spines, which were shorter and thicker than those of *Dimetrodon*, bore side

Number 1, the carnivorous finbacked reptile *Dimetrodon*, 9 to 11 feet long.
Number 2, in the distance, is the plant-eater *Edaphosaurus*.

branches that grew in pairs. A German paleontologist once suggested
that these branches increased the resemblance to horsetails, but
another German thought the spines made *Edaphosaurus* too prickly
to be attacked. The latter theory overlooks the big teeth and strong
jaws of *Dimetrodon*, as well as injuries to spines and other bones of
Edaphosaurus. To *Dimetrodon*, the other reptile must have been
little more than 350 to 600 pounds of unprotected meat.

Unprotected? Yes, for *Edaphosaurus* was a peaceful eater of
clams, snails, and plants. This diet is indicated by the blunt teeth in
his jaws and by broad plates on the floor and roof of his mouth.
These plates, which were studded with buttonlike teeth, crushed
shells readily but could not have been used in a fight.

Some reptiles always look sullen or even malignant; *Dimetrodon*
probably did so. Though not a reptile, *Eryops* was almost as for-

bidding. Varanosaurs combined the alertness of relatively small hunters with apparent eagerness to kill.

Still, life on the Permian deltas probably was no more savage than life in almost any other region at almost any other time. There were plant-eaters, fish-eaters, mud-grubbers, and clam-eaters; there were creatures that hunted for food and others that let it come within reach of their jaws. Few meals were more bloody than a modern tiger's or leopard's, and no Permian reptile was as savage-looking as a Gaboon viper or as deadly as a large rattlesnake.

In short, both life and death on the Permian deltas were normal or even sluggish. They remained so until climatic changes turned the Southwest into deserts of wind-blown sand.

10 LIZARD-HIPPED DINOSAURS

DURING THE 1830s, many sidewalks in western Massachusetts were made of dark red sandstone quarried near the Connecticut River. Some slabs bore odd impressions, and a village doctor sent four of them to Professor Edward Hitchcock, of Amherst College. He described them, in 1836, as "foot marks" that "could not have been made by any other known biped, except birds."

Hitchcock's explanation of his fossils was quite reasonable, for in 1836 nothing was known of reptiles whose feet made birdlike prints with three long toes pointing forward and one very short toe behind. Nor did anyone suspect that dark red sandstones in the Connecticut Valley were 40 to 50 million years older than beds containing fossils of the earliest birds.

Where do these figures place the sandstones in our geologic time scale? They date from the latter half of the Triassic Period, which was the first major division of the Mesozoic Era. It was separated from the Permian Period by an earth-revolution during which more and more sea bottoms became land, more and more land was crumpled into mountain ranges, and mountain ranges were pushed sideways and upward until they broke and rode miles over lower land. Mountains were then worn away, but new ones appeared as long blocks of land broke and tilted, turning one side of each block into a steep-faced highland while the other side became a valley.

By Late Triassic times these highlands and valleys extended from Nova Scotia to North Carolina and perhaps to Florida. We know nothing about plants and animals that lived on the mountains, for they left no fossils. Valleys, however, were the homes of Professor Hitchcock's "birds," which really were dinosaurs.

What Were Dinosaurs?

The word "dinosaur" was coined in 1841, five years after Hitchcock described his fossil footprints. Today, almost everyone knows

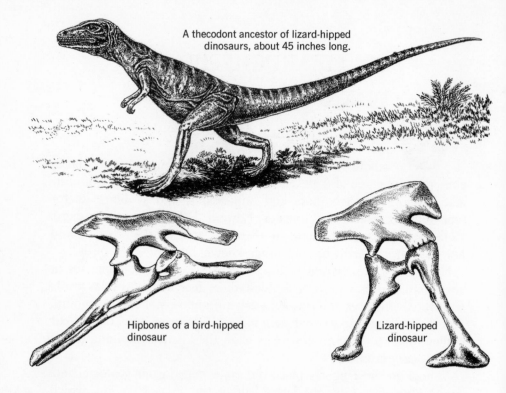

A thecodont ancestor of lizard-hipped
dinosaurs, about 45 inches long.

Hipbones of a bird-hipped
dinosaur

Lizard-hipped
dinosaur

dinosaurs as huge reptiles, long since extinct. One dinosaur has
achieved fame in a comic strip as a caveman's steed.

Three things are wrong with the comic-strip Dinny: he lives 135
million years too late; he gallops about like a horse, and he has plates
of bone along his back and a beak upon his jaws. These errors do no
harm in a "comic," but beak and plates reflect a fault in our everyday
definition and in dictionaries that call dinosaurs one group, or order,
of reptiles that lived during ancient times.

This definition was acceptable many years ago, when fossil
reptiles were just being discovered. But since the 1920s scientists
have known that dinosaurs really belong to two quite separate orders.
One order, the saurischians ("lizard-hips"), is characterized by hipbones essentially like those of lizards and crocodiles. Many lizard-
hips also became very large and had long necks and tails.

Ornithischians ("bird-hips") were never so big, and their hipbones
were built like those of birds. Many bird-hips also had beaks; others
bore upright plates of bone on their backs or were covered by bony

Number 1, a primitive Triassic dinosaur from New Mexico and Arizona. Number 2, a more advanced lizard-hipped reptile from Europe. Both types walked on their hind legs.

armor. The comic-strip Dinny, therefore, combines the plates and beak of typical bird-hips with the huge body, long neck, and very long tail of the largest lizard-hipped dinosaurs.

Though Dinny's size and general build are right for a lizard-hip, not all dinosaurs were giants. Both orders contained members that were no larger than turkeys, and a few were as small as roosters.

Early Lizard-hips

Saurischian dinosaurs evolved during earliest Triassic times, from reptiles called thecodonts. They were lizard-shaped creatures 4 to 5 feet in length, at least half of which was tail. Heads were long and low, forelegs were short, and hind legs were so long that they alone were used for walking and running. When thecodonts ran they leaned far forward and held their tails out stiffly to balance their bodies.

Thecodonts ranged across Africa, Europe, and Asia during Early

Triassic times, and then spread through the Americas. In the meantime saurischians evolved and soon followed thecodonts to the New World. Their descendants made virtually all the footprints preserved in Late Triassic valleys of the East, but few petrified bones have been found there. Fortunately, other primitive lizard-hips left their skeletons in Late Triassic deposits of northwestern New Mexico and northeastern Arizona.

The word dinosaur means "terrible reptile," but there was nothing terrible about these creatures. They were bipeds 7 or 8 feet long and 3 feet tall, with narrow pointed heads, slender necks, deep but narrow bodies, and long tails. The hind legs were long but not stilt-like, with three long toes in front and one short toe behind. The forelegs were short but not useless; the weight was 40 or 50 pounds. These reptiles must have roamed wooded uplands, preying upon smaller reptiles that have not yet been discovered. Though victims could be held with the forefeet, the dinosaurs probably captured food with their long, sharp-toothed jaws.

These southwestern dinosaurs lived at about the time Hitchcock's fossil footprints were being made in the East. Many of the eastern dinosaurs probably resembled those of New Mexico and Arizona, though some kinds had shorter skulls. Eastern dinosaurs also preferred river valleys to uplands, leaving tracks on moist bottom lands and sandbanks. Now and then a reptile sat down on wet sand or crossed a spot where the sediment was so soft that the little hind toes left their marks. Less frequently, a lizard-hip stopped so suddenly that the tips of its toes dug into the sand.

Most of these footprints can be mistaken for bird tracks, for the feet of early lizard-hips were more birdlike than were those of ornithischians. Most footprints also were made by reptiles 6 to 12 feet in length that walked on their hind legs and ate meat. Some prints, however, are 12 to 18 inches long and represent animals that probably reached lengths of 16 to 20 feet and weights of 3000 to 5000 pounds. In Europe, actual remains of dinosaurs reach similar size. One species was a big-headed carnivore; another was a small-headed herbivore which probably held plants between the forefeet while it bit off tender stems. The forelegs were longer and stronger than those of most Triassic dinosaurs. Apparently plant-eating dinosaurs were beginning to turn into quadrupeds, thus reversing the trend established by their thecodont ancestors.

Diplodocus (1) was the longest dinosaur known; it measured 80 to 87 feet. *Apatosaurus* (2), also called *Brontosaurus*, or "thunder" lizard, was shorter but heavier. Both kinds lived on the Morrison lowlands.

The Age of Giants

Our tale now skips about 45 million years, to the country around Bone Cabin, in Wyoming, as the Jurassic Period was closing. The land, now 6000 to 7000 feet high, then was part of a low, moist plain that extended from Montana to New Mexico, and from South Dakota to Utah. Sluggish rivers that came from mountains far to the west carried sand and mud to the plain, depositing them in shifting channels, on bottom lands, and in lakes. These deposits, which make up the Morrison Formation, range from dull gray to yellowish brown, pink, blue-gray, and lavender.

Since the flood plain lay just west of a sea, its climate was both warm and humid. Between its rivers it was covered with forests where conifers mingled with maidenhair trees, palmlike cycads, and tree ferns. As fossils, however, plants are outranked by dinosaurs, which number sixty-nine named species. During life, these reptiles ranged from 6-foot hunters that resembled those of Triassic Arizona to plant-eaters that were 40 to almost 90 feet long and 25 to 44 feet tall, and weighed 15 to 50 tons.

These giants were descended from the large Triassic herbivore of Europe or its close relatives. We therefore find a general resemblance among these creatures, even though no two were exactly alike. All had long necks and very long tails, which were thick at the base and ended in whiplash tips. Most heads were blunt and teeth were weak; one dinosaur whose head was 2 feet long had teeth that looked like pencil stubs. Bodies were big and barrel-shaped, and hind legs still were longer than forelegs, though the former were 5 to 9 feet high. The feet were round and thickly padded, and had lost parts of some or all toes.

The biggest of these bizarre creatures did depart from this general plan. Its tail was shorter than its neck; its forelegs were longer than the hind legs, and its body sloped backward from shoulders to hips. The upper "arm" bone, or humerus, was 7 to 8 feet long. This, by the way, was no freakish giant, but an ordinary member of a type that ranged from Wyoming and Colorado to Tanzania (Tanganyika) in eastern Africa.

There has been great argument as to how these dinosaurs lived. Long-established theory says that they could not go on land, where the ends of their leg bones would have been crushed under their

Skull, 30 inches long

Brachiosaurus was the largest Late Jurassic dinosaur; it ranged from eastern Africa to southern Colorado.

tremendous weight. Since the reptiles could not walk on land, they waded and let water help support their bodies. Often they went into water so deep that only the tops of their heads reached the surface. They could breathe because their nostrils were higher than their eyes. Females let their eggs develop inside their bodies instead of trying to lay them on land.

No one doubts that big dinosaurs could wade, or that they sometimes went into deep water. But several authorities insist that they also waded in water too shallow to reach their bellies, and on muddy ground. The difference has been traced in footprints that are deep and indistinct where water was deep, shallow and clear-cut in shoals, and still sharper on muddy ground. At Bandera, Texas, footprints show that twenty-three mature and half-grown reptiles splashed in shallows, and were followed by carnivores. Neither they nor the half-grown plant-feeders could have walked in water deep enough to support fully grown reptiles that weighed 30 tons or more. At Glen Rose, also in Texas, a carnivorous dinosaur followed and even stepped in the footprints of an herbivore that apparently walked on a muddy seashore. Again, the carnivore could not have waded in water deep enough to half-float his prey.

The idea that herbivorous dinosaurs ate only soft plants has also been qualified. Petrified stomach contents found in east-central Utah contain broken twigs and branches and many bits of bone. Perhaps giant dinosaurs had to have so much food that they took everything they could find. Succulent stems and leaves were good, but woody plants served almost as well and meat was acceptable. It may have come as carrion; even if the reptile walked on land, it could hardly have been a hunter.

Whatever these dinosaurs did, they did almost automatically. Skull cavities show that brains were small, weighing a pound or less in reptiles with total weights of 30 to 35 tons. The shapes of these little brains show that dinosaurs smelled well, heard well, and possessed a good sense of balance; each reptile had a good idea of what was going on around him and knew when his body was safely and comfortably upright or when it tipped dangerously. But the routine movements of walking, wading, striking out with the legs, and swinging the tail were not determined by the brain. As we learned in Chapter 2, these matters were managed unconsciously by greatly enlarged ganglia above the shoulders and hips.

Horned dinosaur

Allosaurus, a meat-eater of the Morrison lowlands, was 34 feet long and had a 3-foot head. The horned dinosaur was not quite so large.

Little and Big Meat-eaters

The first dinosaurs were hunters that fed upon other reptiles, most of which were small. As epochs went by, some hunters grew large—large enough to kill and eat the most massive herbivores. Other hunters, however, became almost birdlike and probably ate everything from insects to dinosaur eggs and fruit. A fossil found in Mongolia apparently belongs to one of these creatures that was killed in the act of robbing another dinosaur's nest.

Birdlike hunters lived during Late Cretaceous times, but other meat-eaters ranged the Morrison lowlands and hunted along the seacoast in Texas. Some seem too small for their times; others were big, with deep heads and long hind legs whose feet were armed with powerful claws. The forelegs and feet were small and the tail, which remained a balancing organ, was both thick and long.

This description is generalized; it fits a whole group of lizard-hipped hunters that ranged through Africa, Europe, Asia, and North America. In Morrison forests they were best represented by *Allosaurus*, a creature 30 to 34 feet long, with a 3-foot head and 6-inch teeth. Another hunter, which lived in Colorado, was 17 feet high and had a blunt horn on its nose.

These big reptiles were not the kind of hunter that lay in wait for victims to pass and then pounced upon them. Morrison meat-eaters stalked their game, though probably not for long distances. When they found it, they attacked with a rush; to have leaped upon their prey would have meant tearing their legs to pieces. Killing was done with the teeth; the forelegs were too small to be useful, and the dinosaur had to stand on its hind legs. The huge feet, with their massive claws, held prey once it was down; the teeth, which had done the killing, sheared great chunks of meat from the bones. If a few teeth broke off, as they frequently did, new ones soon grew in their places and kept the jaws ready for use.

11   BIRD-HIPS IN BEAKS
AND ARMOR

ALLOSAURS ATE big herbivores, for the marks of teeth still appear on their bones. But when giants were not at hand to be killed, carnivores hunted smaller species that belonged to the order of bird-hipped dinosaurs.

Among these reptiles, the term bird-hipped does not mean "birdlike." We have seen that early lizard-hipped dinosaurs had hind feet that left birdlike tracks. Many of their bones also were hollow, another trait that is characteristic of birds. But the bones of bird-hips were almost solid, the hind feet were broad and heavy, and their claws had often turned into hoofs.

Two Unspecialized Bird-hips

Bird-hipped dinosaurs on which carnivores most frequently preyed were primitive members of their order. Several species have been described under the general name of *Camptosaurus*, but their only important differences are in size. It seems likely, therefore, that they represent a single species that reached lengths of 15 to 17 feet, and that so-called species 4 to 5 feet long are merely young ones.

Whether young or adult, one species or several, all camptosaurs were bipeds that walked on strong, thick hind legs. The forelegs, however, were longer than those of carnivorous lizard-hips, and easily rested on the ground when the reptiles ate low-growing plants. The head was low and long, and the front of the mouth was toothless. A short beak took the place of teeth in nipping stems, leaves, and fruits.

Camptosaurs outlived *Allosaurus* but in North America, at least, the former seem to have produced no descendants. In western Europe, relatives of *Camptosaurus* gave rise to larger, but still unspecialized, bird-hips which were the first dinosaurs to be recognized and named as reptiles. They were discovered in March 1822 by the wife of a British doctor who liked to go riding with her husband when he visited patients in the country. While Dr. Mantell was in one house, Mrs. Mantell found a petrified tooth in a pile of stones beside the road. Her husband discovered several bones as well as additional teeth.

Anatomists were rare in those days, and anatomists who knew fossils numbered one—Baron Georges Cuvier, of Paris. Dr. Mantell sent his specimens to the Baron, who said the teeth belonged to an extinct rhinoceros and the bones to a hippopotamus. An Oxford dean accepted these identifications, but Dr. Mantell knew that his specimens had come from rocks too old to contain hippopotami and

A primitive bird-hipped dinosaur of the American West, and *Iguanodon* of Europe. Both lived during the Cretaceous Period.

rhinos. He kept on trying to find out what they were, and in 1825 met a naturalist who showed him that the fossil teeth resembled those of Mexican lizards called iguanas. With this hint, Mantell described his fossils as the remains of a large extinct reptile which he appropriately named *Iguanodon*, or "iguana tooth."

Although *Iguanodon* was discovered in England, its most famous fossils came from Early Cretaceous rocks of Belgium. There a coal mine reached a one-time fissure into which seventeen of these reptiles had fallen while they were browsing or running from carnivores. The skeletons belonged to animals 30 to 34 feet long and 18 feet tall when they stood erect. Hind legs were long and heavy, but the forelegs were shorter than those of camptosaurs. The head was long and low, with a short beak at the front of the mouth. The teeth were arranged in several rows; they had sawlike edges but were worn flat, which shows that they crushed gritty plants such as horsetails. Ligaments on the back and tail were bony. They gave strength, but they must have made it hard for the reptile to bend his body or swing his tail.

Another group of bird-hips began in England but prospered in North America. The early British form was a heavy creature about

Hip ganglion

Brain

Stegosaurus, an armored bird-hip of the Morrison lowlands. At the left are the hip ganglion and brain, drawn on the same scale.

13 feet long and 4 feet high at the shoulder, and its leathery skin was set with rows of bony plates. This reptile lived in Early Jurassic times and apparently remained in Europe, but *Stegosaurus*, its most famous descendant, wandered through Morrison woodlands. Full-grown stegosaurs were 18 to 25 feet long, stood 10 to 13 feet high above the hips, and walked on all fours in spite of the fact that the forelegs were less than half as long as the hind legs. The head was low and very small; the jaws bore a beak as well as crushing teeth, and the body was deep but narrow. The creature was unable to run away from danger but defended itself by swinging its tail, which was armed with long, bony spikes.

The value of those spikes is clear; when swung by the powerful tail muscles, they could crush the ribs or rip the underside of an attacking meat-eater—even one as strong as *Allosaurus*. But we are less sure about broad bony plates that ran in two rows along the back. Perhaps they warded off attacks from above, but what was this worth when the dinosaur's sides had little or no protection?

Part of *Stegosaurus'* fame comes from those plates and his spines, which show well in pictures and on a life-size model that has been displayed for many years in the United States National Museum. But countless people who never saw that model know *Stegosaurus* as the dinosaur "famous in prehistoric lore" because it had two sets of brains

> One in his head (the usual place),
> the other at his spinal base.

In actual fact, the second "brain" was the sacral, or hip, ganglion, and another was located between the shoulders. Both were larger than the actual brain, which lay in the skull and was about the size of a walnut. Both ganglia were much larger than that, and the one between the hips weighed more than 3 pounds. Its large size may reflect the extent to which *Stegosaurus* relied upon his hind legs to keep his tail toward his enemies, and upon the tail itself to strike blows that beat off hungry predators.

Duckbills of Alberta

The low, damp Morrison plains were a favored habitat of stegosaurs. Two other groups of bird-hipped dinosaurs reached their

Numbers 1 and 2, two duckbilled dinosaurs of Late Cretaceous Alberta. Number 3 is a lizard-hipped species that resembled an ostrich, except for its long tail.

zenith on moist Late Cretaceous deltas which now are badlands along the Red Deer River, in the Canadian province of Alberta.

Today the region in which the badlands have been cut is high and usually dry wheat-farming country in which fields are broken only by roads and houses may be miles apart. The Red Deer River flows eastward from the Rockies and then southward, eroding a valley that has deepened and spread into badlands which are less spectacular than some but are world-famous for their bird-hipped dinosaurs.

Most badlands form where rain water falls upon soft or weak rocks that can be easily worn away. Beds in the Red Deer Badlands meet this condition, for they are pink, buff, and gray clays that alternate with rusty-brown sandstones and layers of volcanic ash. Most of them settled almost 70 million years ago, on deltas built into a shallow

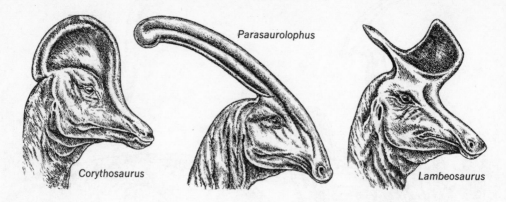

Heads of three duckbilled dinosaurs from the Red Deer Badlands of Alberta.

sea by streams from the then-new Rocky Mountains. Large parts of those deltas were swampy, and lagoons formed where sand bars separated shallow bays from the sea.

Rocks tell what the deltas looked like; fossil plants show that their climate was warm to subtropical. Poplar, oak, and sassafras grew on high ground near the mountains, but palms, screw pines, magnolias, and figs were found among the swamps. There seem to have been many moist prairies, but they may have been covered with herbs, not grass.

The most abundant reptiles on the Red Deer prairies were duckbilled dinosaurs. From a distance they looked like iguanodonts 22 to 40 feet long, 13 to 18 feet tall when they stood upright, and 6 to 10 feet high at the hips when they rested on all fours to feed. Flattened tails which, like the backs, were strengthened by bony ligaments made up almost half of their length.

The heads of these creatures explain their English name. All had jaws with closely set banks of teeth whose number ranged from 800 in some species to 1600 in others. The teeth cut and crushed coarse, gritty plants, but those plants were broken or pulled by broad bills, like the bills of vastly oversized ducks. Bills could also be used to grub and shovel food from the muddy bottoms of rivers, swamps, and lagoons.

Duckbilled dinosaurs could stand upright; they must have done so again and again as they looked, listened, and sniffed for danger. In walking, they leaned far forward, with their bodies balanced by their tails. The webbed toes on their forefeet had small hoofs; the three toes on their big hind feet apparently were not webbed and bore hoofs as wide as those of a horse. The whole body was covered by tough, wrinkled skin set with hard scales that did not overlap. Except in size, they resembled the scales of modern lizards called Gila monsters.

We know that brain cavities in skulls give clues to the senses and intelligence of fossils. Duckbills were not bright—no reptile is—but their brains weighed as much as the brains of herbivorous giants many times heavier. Hearing, smell, and eyesight were keen; these senses, combined with good nervous control, enabled duckbills to discover enemies and escape by dashing into water. There they swam by sculling with their tails, beyond the reach of pursuers.

Duckbilled dinosaurs belonged to three types: flat-headed, solid-crested, and hollow-crested. Solid crests now resemble horns, but they probably were covered with skin and could hardly have been weapons. Hollow crests make us think of ancient helmets, whose crests served as decorations and stopped blows from swords. But we have no reason to think that duckbill crests were ornamental, for they were not limited to one sex, like the antlers of deer or the peacock's showy "tail." Nor did crests stop blows from enemies, for the dinosaurs that fed on duckbills attacked with biting teeth, not swords. Hollow crests, moreover, were weakened by nasal passages that wound through them or expanded into air-filled chambers. These empty spaces may have provided space for smelling, but we really do not know how they were used.

Armor, Shields, and Horns

Duckbills ran or swam away from danger, but armored dinosaurs of the Red Deer deltas withstood it by lying down. They were low-slung, massive, broad-bodied creatures; one called *Ankylosaurus* was 16 feet long and at least 5 feet wide, but stood less than 5 feet high. Its 27-inch skull looked like a block of bone; its back was covered with bony plates, and thick spines grew along the sides. The tail ended in a rounded mass of bone at the end of stiffly interlocked vertebrae. When *Ankylosaurus* crouched against the ground he was almost impregnable. Any carnivore that attacked from the front or side could do little more than break some teeth on the ankylosaur's skull and plated armor. If the attacker came from the rear, his breath would be knocked from him and his bones battered by that club-shaped tail.

Another group of bird-hipped dinosaurs was built to meet danger head-on. They had sharp beaks and one or more horns; the skull spread backward over the neck in a multipurpose shield. Jaw muscles

Typical dinosaurs that lived in Montana and nearby parts of the West near the end of Cretaceous times. Number 1, the duckbill *Anatosaurus*, also called *Trachodon*. Number 2, *Triceratops* warding off an attack. Number 3, the armor-plated *Ankylosaurus*, which defended itself by crouching on the ground. Number 4, *Tyrannosaurus*, a meat-eater 47 feet long.

were attached to its base; behind them came muscles that moved the entire head. These muscles and those of the shoulders were protected by the shield as long as a horned dinosaur faced its enemies.

Horned, shield-bearing dinosaurs originated in Asia; one primitive type became famous during the 1920s, when its nests and eggs with

unhatched young were found in Mongolia. This early species reached lengths of 5 to 6 feet; its horn was only a nubbin, and the shield had two large openings that probably were covered by skin. Later members of the group became 10, 18 and even 25 feet long; their legs as well as their bodies grew heavy and their beaks and horns were sharp. Skulls measured 5 to 8 feet from snout to rim of shield, which often was set with spikes.

At the End of an Era

The largest shield-bearers introduce us to dinosaurian life in the Northwest at the end of the Mesozoic Era. There were no great lizard-hipped herbivores; if any still existed—and there are hints that they did—they ranged 1300 miles to the southward and into South America. Allosaurs and horned meat-eaters were missing, too, as were ornately crested duckbills and horned dinosaurs with long or recurved spikes on their shields.

What remained? Two of the largest horned dinosaurs and one massive armored species. Flat-headed duckbills also were common, and a lizard-hipped hunter that must have resembled a long-tailed ostrich in scales. It probably ate many different things, though its favorite food may have been eggs.

Finally there was *Tyrannosaurus*, a distant relative of allosaurs and the largest of land-dwelling carnivores. He was 47 feet long, 18 feet tall, and weighed 8 to 10 tons. His head was 50 inches in length, his mouth had a 2-foot gape, and his hind feet bore 8-inch claws. The forelegs, like those of allosaurs, were small.

Big bodies require big meals and, if the giant is a reptile, food must not be hard to get. *Tyrannosaurus* probably relied on duckbills, which were big, defenseless, and plentiful. When they were not available, however, *Tyrannosaurus* apparently attacked horned dinosaurs. The most likely victim, since it was abundant, was *Triceratops*.

In words the two seem unevenly matched; a 47-foot hunter with 6-inch teeth against a 25-foot herbivore. These are only dimensions, however, and these dinosaurs did not battle by matching measurements. *Triceratops* was no slow, peace-seeking dullard; for a reptile he was alert, with a brain more than twice as large as that of his enemy. *Triceratops* also had a sharp beak, a short horn on his nose, and two long ones above the eyes. An upward thrust of those horns could disembowel an attacker that came head-on.

A head-on fight, moreover, was just what *Triceratops* sought. His hind legs formed closely spaced columns on which he could pivot; his forelegs spread widely and firmly as he thrust his head forward. His bony shield absorbed bites directed toward the powerful neck muscles that raised and swung his head. No matter how often *Tyrannosaurus* might walk around him, *Triceratops* always faced his enemy with a shield and weapons that could not be beaten down. Most fights probably ended when *Tyrannosaurus* gave up and went away to find a weaker victim. *Triceratops* merely stayed where he was, dozing or munching plants.

Triceratops was built to resist the attacks of big hunters, but he also used his horns in quarrels with other horned dinosaurs. Petrified shields bear scars too deep and wide to have been made by teeth of *Tyrannosaurus*. Males of *Triceratops* probably fought during the mating season, since plant-eaters seldom quarrel over food.

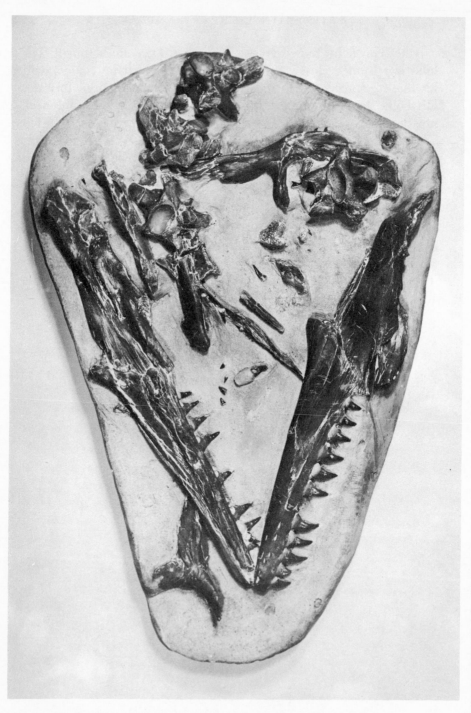

Jaws, teeth, and bones of a mosasaur from Late Cretaceous rocks of western Kansas. This specimen is in the museum of Princeton University.

12   REPTILES TO THE SEA

REPTILES BEGAN to leave fresh water as soon as they found food on land, and for almost a quarter of a billion years they dominated terrestrial life. During that time, however, several groups went back to the water. Some even competed with sharks and ancestral tarpons as masters of life in the sea.

This seems strange until we recall the fact that animals will invade any kind of surroundings to which they can fit themselves *if those surroundings offer them a living.* Seas made that offer again and again, and four-legged reptiles that could become swimmers repeatedly took advantage of it.

Turtles, Placodonts, and Crocodiles

When aquatic reptiles are mentioned, we usually think of turtles. They may have been the first reptiles to go back to water, for one of their ancestors has been found in Middle Permian rocks of South Africa. True turtles appeared in Early Triassic times, when they swam in ponds and lakes of Europe.

These turtles lived only in fresh water, and it has been the principal home of their successors and descendants. Many of them, indeed, went back to land; our desert tortoise and box turtle show how well they fared when they did so. In time, others took to the sea, where plenty of space and the support provided by water permitted them to reach large size. Marine turtles that lived in Late Cretaceous seas of the West reached lengths of 8 to 12 feet and weights of 1200 to 3000 pounds. Their principal food seems to have been ammonoids and other horn-shells. Though admirably adapted to swimming, these reptiles crawled clumsily and slowly when they went ashore.

Another group of aquatic reptiles seems to have come from Permian forest-dwellers that may have climbed trees. As the Triassic Period began, descendants called placodonts took to sea when they dived to feed on thick-shelled mollusks. These reptiles had blunt heads, plump bodies, thin tails, and paddle-shaped legs. Tails were flexible and could be used in swimming, but the body was rigid.

Stiff bodies are often armored, and early placodonts had bony plates that seem to have been the first stage of armor for the back. On the belly were many abdominal ribs which joined at the midline, overlapped, and bent abruptly upward at the sides. Though they did not form a solid shield, they gave great strength to the undersurface and protected it from injury.

Some marine placodonts developed bony shells, and so both looked and lived like turtles. Strangest of all, however, was *Henodus*, which lived in Late Triassic swamps and lakes of southern Germany. *Henodus* had a broadly flattened carapace of bone and a blunt, broad snout. All except two flat teeth had vanished; the jaws contained plates that apparently resembled whalebone. They must have been used to catch small crustaceans that swam in hordes through the water in which *Henodus* lived.

Like many horn-shells, crocodiles appeared because evolution repeated itself. It also forced the new reptiles to compete with others that already were large, strong, and common.

The first known members of the order Crocodilia were armored reptiles about 30 inches long that lived in northeastern Arizona during Late Triassic times. They walked safely over low sandy ground, and they seem to have met few enemies in ponds and small, shallow streams. Elsewhere they encountered larger, stronger, and more abundant reptiles which are known as phytosaurs because an early scientist thought they ate plants. Actually, phytosaurs were reptiles related to thecodonts which assumed the shapes and habits of crocodiles some 30 million years before crocodiles themselves evolved. By Late Triassic times, phytosaurs ranged from 8 to 20 feet in length and had powerful swimming tails. Their narrow jaws were set with 180 to more than 300 sharp teeth, which could capture both fish and reptiles. Only the nostrils, which were near the eyes, gave conspicuous proof that phytosaurs were not crocodiles.

True crocodiles could not fight such creatures; they could only keep out of the way. This they did till phytosaurs died out when the Triassic Period ended. As they vanished new kinds of crocodiles evolved, and some of them went to sea. Remains of species 12 to 20 feet long have been found in Jurassic marine deposits and continue through Early Cretaceous formations. Many fossils show typical long-

Placodus, a marine reptile of early Triassic age, was 5 to 8 feet 6 inches long. It swam and dived near shore to feed on clams and other mollusks.

snouted crocodiles with plated skins, narrow tails, and legs that could be used for walking. The geosaurs, however, were slender, smooth-skinned reptiles whose legs were good only for balancing and whose tails were equipped with fins.

Fish, Men, or Fish-reptiles?

Besides turtles and placodonts, another important group of reptiles went to live in Triassic seas. There they became so well adapted to water that in 1699 an Oxford curator described them as fish developed from eggs which storms had driven into the rocks. A German disagreed; to him they were remains of human beings drowned by the flood that carried Noah's Ark to Mount Ararat. More than a century later, another German named the fossils ichthyosaurs, or "fish-saurians," as if they swam with tail in one group and head in the other.

These fossils came from Jurassic deposits; those found in older beds are not so highly specialized. Middle Triassic rocks of California and Nevada contain remains of ichthyosaurs with torpedo-shaped bodies and long reptilian tails. The jaws are not very long and the tails seem to have had folds of skin above and below instead of fins.

Ichthyosaurs became more and more fishlike during the latter half of Triassic times. Early Jurassic "slates" of southwestern Germany (they really are hard shales) contain ichthyosaurs that had sharklike bodies, long narrow jaws, and big round eyes. The backbone bent

Henodus, 3 to 4 feet long, had a broad turtlelike shell made of bony plates. This reptile lived in swamps, lakes, and broad sluggish streams.

downward in the tail; a broad fin grew upward and another fin had appeared on the back. Some specimens include carbonized fins and flesh; the skin was almost bare of scales and was dark on the back and sides but whitish on the undersurface.

Ichthyosaurs probably never ventured on land, where their flippers would have been useless. In the sea they were strong, swift swimmers that ranged round the world during Late Jurassic and Cretaceous times. They fed largely on fish and belemnoids. Perhaps they also ate small ichthyosaurs, but skeletons found in abdomens seem to belong to unhatched young ones that had developed in the mother's body and were smothered when she died. Eggs must have hatched inside the mother, since she could not go ashore to lay them.

"Near-saurians"; the Plesiosaurs

The German "shales" that are rich in fish-lizards also contain plesiosaurs. This name, which means "almost" or "near-saurians," was devised in 1821 by an English clergyman who was also a geolo-

Geosaurus, a smooth-skinned marine crocodile, had webbed feet and a fin on its tail.

gist. He thought the fossils were more truly reptilian than were ichthyosaurs.

Plesiosaurs belonged to two groups, the short-necked and the long-necked. The former had plump bodies and heads with long jaws; the latter were very broad of body and long of neck, though their heads were short. One species had 76 vertebrae in the neck, but a short-necked plesiosaur had only 13. Tails were not very useful in swimming, but the legs and feet had become long paddles which the reptiles used as if they were oars.

Though plesiosaurs were common in Jurassic seas of Europe, they were rare in other parts of the world. Then, during Cretaceous times, plesiosaurs spread around the earth, and some kinds also became very large. Species 50 feet long swam over Australia and the American West. The Australian species was much the larger, for its neck was short. The neck of the American *Elasmosaurus* was 23 feet long. With the head and the tail, it made up more than two thirds of the reptile's length.

Big plesiosaurs swam in open seas; species of medium to small size went into bays, rivers, and swampy lagoons. Their bones have been found in the Red Deer Badlands, where remains of bird-hipped dinosaurs are common.

When plesiosaurs became fossils, the contents of their stomachs were sometimes preserved. They include bones of fish and other reptiles, remains of belemnoids, and worn gizzard stones. The reptile mentioned in Chapter 2, which swallowed pebbles near Minnesota but died in western Kansas, was a plesiosaur.

Number 1, a Triassic ichthyosaur, or "fish-lizard," that swam in seas of California and Nevada. Number 2, *Ophthalmosaurus*, from Late Cretaceous rocks of western Kansas, resembled Jurassic ichthyosaurs that swam in European seas.

Lizards of the Sea; the Mosasaurs

The Maas, or Meuse, which Romans called the Mosa, is a river that flows past the city of Maastricht, Holland. There, in 1780, quarrymen found a skull that was first thought to belong to a whale, but was finally recognized as a sea-lizard and was named *Mosasaurus*. Its closest living relatives are the monitors of Africa, Asia, Australia, and Polynesia.

Some groups of reptiles live for ages, but mosasaurs began, evolved, and died out within the Cretaceous Period. Their history as full-fledged mosasaurs may amount to less than 30 million years.

If mosasaurs had lived longer they might have become as varied as lizard-hipped dinosaurs were. As it was, all mosasaurs remained slender, long-bodied reptiles with flat, pointed heads and long swimming tails. For steering and balancing they used broad, rather stubby

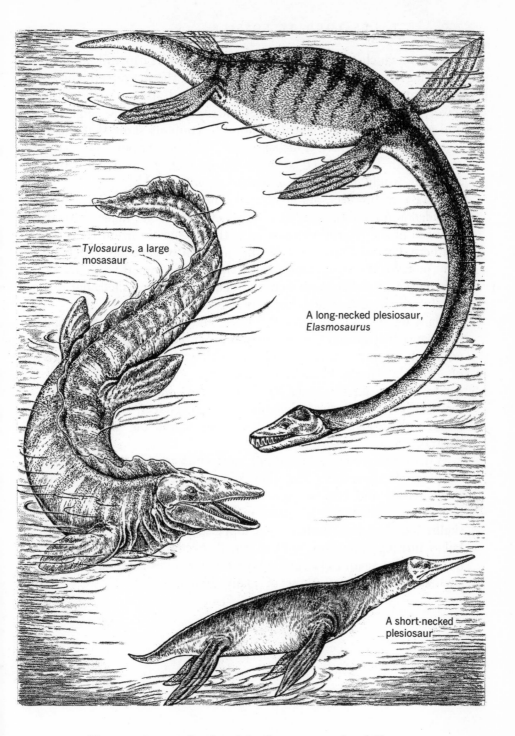

Three marine reptiles found in Cretaceous rocks of Kansas

flippers in which bones of the original legs and feet can still be made out. Rings of thin bones strengthened the eyes; the sharp teeth curved backward, and the lower jaw could be dropped and spread like the lower jaw of a snake. This allowed mosasaurs to swallow large fish and good-sized reptiles. Petrified stomach contents show that mosasaurs sometimes killed *Portheus*, the "bulldog tarpon," a sharp-toothed fish that reached a length of 12 feet. Even a half-grown *Portheus* would have been a dangerous mouthful.

Mosasaurs, however, did not always dine on vertebrates. Their prey included ammonoids, some of whose shells bear holes made by teeth arranged in the typical mosasaurian pattern. One sea lizard from the southern United States and Europe apparently gave up vertebrate prey in favor of crustaceans, snails, clams, and oysterlike mollusks. The reptile's bulblike teeth were excellent for crushing shells but useless for catching fish or other active swimmers.

Many big fossils come from the West, and we expect giants among mosasaurs that ranged Cretaceous seas from Texas to northern Canada. Instead, most western species are 18 to 26 feet long, and skulls of even the largest kinds look surprisingly delicate. The Atlantic coastal region, on the other hand, has fossils whose long jaws and massive vertebrae indicate lengths of 35 to 45 feet. Though more slender, these giants were almost as long as the big plesiosaur of Australia.

Whether they were giants or not, mosasaurs apparently had savage tempers. We have seen that they killed large, dangerous fish, but many scored and broken bones indicate that the reptiles also attacked each other. These bones include vertebrae, ribs, jaws, and skulls; toes had been bitten from flippers, and a large part of one tail is missing. The skin, with its small, overlapping scales, offered no protection against creatures whose teeth were as sharp and whose jaws were as strong as those of many dinosaurs.

13 FOUR WORLDS OF FLIGHT

WHEN FLYING animals are mentioned, we think of bats, birds, and insects. Fossils add a fourth major group, made up of winged reptiles.

Fossil bats are too rare to demand much of our attention. All are less than 70 million years old; the best ones are found in deposits that settled in large, shallow lakes where the bats sometimes dashed into water as they hunted insects. When we think how seldom bats make that error today, we do not wonder that their fossils are exceedingly rare.

Insects, the First Flyers

Though fossil insects are not abundant, their history is a long one. It began with wingless, and therefore flightless, springtails that hopped among plants in Middle Devonian bogs. Wings began as flaps of skin on each side of the body; by Pennsylvanian times they had developed into the folding wings of cockroaches and the widely spread, non-foldable wings of "ancestral dragonflies." These creatures, which looked like dragonflies but were not, became 28 to 30 inches wide and 12 to 15 inches long. Pennsylvanian cockroaches also were large: 4 to 6 inches in length, exclusive of their antennae, or "feelers."

More advanced insects, such as crickets, May flies, beetles, butterflies, and wasps, appeared during Permian and later ages. Many fossils show color markings on the wings; a Permian relative of crickets also reveals large chirping organs. The richest American deposits of fossil insects lie in beds of hardened volcanic ash that settled during Oligocene times and are named for Florissant, Colorado, near which good exposures are found. The Florissant beds also contain many imprints of leaves and petrified redwood stumps.

Ramphorhynchus

Pterodactylus

Long-tailed and short-tailed pterosaurs. Both lived in Europe during Jurassic times.

Reptiles with Wings

Flying reptiles, or pterosaurs, were discovered in southern Germany. The fossils came from rocks of Late Jurassic age—a time when the region was a warm, shallow sea dotted with coral reefs which formed shoals and low islands. Small islands probably were barren; large ones were covered with groves in which palmlike cycads mingled with trees related to modern monkey-puzzle and Norfolk Island "pines." Ferns grew on the ground and insects were plentiful. Among them were true dragonflies whose wings spread more than 4 inches.

Dragonflies preyed on small insects, and the smallest pterosaurs sometimes caught dragonflies. Usually, however, the reptiles ate fish that swam at the surface of quiet lagoons. Schools of jellyfish swam there, too, along with shrimps, squids, and ammonoids. When these creatures died they sank to the bottom and were covered with fine-grained mud that became evenly bedded white or cream-colored limestone.

That limestone has been quarried since Roman times, but the first pterosaur was described in 1784. The author called it a marine animal and mistook its wings for fins. A professor from Strasbourg

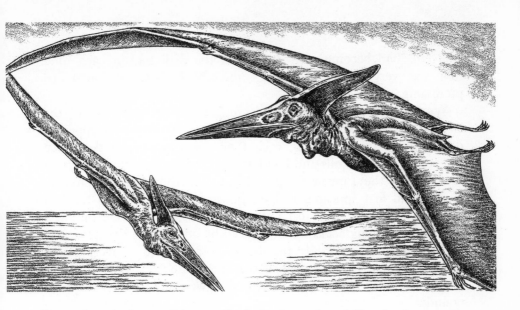

Pteranodon, the largest flying reptile, had a long, sharp bill and a bony crest on its head.

disagreed: To him the fossil formed a link between birds and bats. Another professor pronounced it a water bird, and a fourth savant said it was a bat. Meanwhile, Baron Cuvier all but solved the problem by calling the fossil a flying lizard. He also named it *Pterodactylus*, which means "wing-finger."

Two groups of pterosaurs lived on the ancient German islands. The more primitive group contained reptiles with long, low, pointed heads whose jaws were set with well-developed teeth. The slender tail was much longer than the body; in some species the tail had an upright flap of skin at its end. The short hind legs ended in five-toed feet, but each foreleg had become a wing covered with skin that stretched from the body, ankle, and shoulder to the tip of the very long fourth "finger." The fifth had disappeared, and the first three fingers were clawlike structures which the reptiles probably used when they climbed. In resting, pterosaurs seem to have hung head downward, holding to branches or rough bark with their feet.

The second group of pterosaurs, which was typified by *Pterodactylus*, included species as small as most sparrows and others which were the largest members of their order. All had long, slender heads and jaws that either were set with delicate teeth or were toothless.

The tails had become mere stubs and the fifth toe on each hind foot was very small. The wings resembled those of long-tailed pterosaurs.

We have called the long-tailed group the more primitive of the two; it was also the more ancient. Long-tailed pterosaurs appeared during Early Jurassic times; even then some types had developed big but very light skulls and had lost many of their teeth. The group died out as the Jurassic Period closed, but short-tailed pterosaurs (which had first appeared in Late Jurassic times) lived on through the Cretaceous Period. Most Late Cretaceous species were toothless reptiles whose long beaks were balanced by bony crests that extended backward. In some kinds the wings spread 6 to 7 feet; others reached 25 feet. In spite of their size they were not heavy, for their long bones were hollow and their bodies weighed 12 to perhaps 50 pounds.

The largest of these creatures, *Pteranodon,* was most abundant in western Kansas during Late Cretaceous times. Remains of more than 500 individuals have been found in marine limestones that contain sea turtles, mosasaurs, and the largest of long-necked plesiosaurs.

Every expert is sure that pterosaurs flew, but no one knows just how they did so. One problem is posed by the breastbone, which did not provide attachment for powerful muscles like those that move the wings of birds. A second problem comes from the fact that flight, which seems like an effortless way to travel, takes much more energy than walking or swimming. Birds get that energy by living at a rapid rate, as can be told by feeling the heat of their bodies and timing the beats of their hearts. But pterosaurs were cold-blooded reptiles. How could they obtain energy to beat their skin-covered wings?

Theorists once held that pterosaurs did not beat their wings; that they climbed trees, released their hold, and glided forth to capture fish. Having done so, they tilted their wings, soared back to their perches, and repeated the performance.

This theory failed for several reasons. It now seems that small pterosaurs got into the air by fluttering, glided when they could—as in swooping down to catch fish—and got back to their trees by fluttering again. If this did not take them as high as they wanted to go, they used the claws on their wings to climb.

Pteranodon, however, was too big to flutter; he must have beaten his wings vigorously before he began to glide. He also beat his wings to regain altitude, and he beat them very vigorously indeed after plunging his head into sea water to snap up food. He had to become air-borne in a hurry, for if he did not do so he would drown.

Many pteranodons probably did drown; this is the most likely explanation for their numerous fossils. But for millions of years, greater numbers lived. Regardless of theories and problems, their big wings *must* have been used.

The fact that varied pterosaurs lived and flew throughout Jurassic and much of Cretaceous times has led some authorities to suggest that they were not as coldly reptilian as they seem. Perhaps their hearts were partly birdlike and pumped warmish blood through their bodies. Pterosaurs may also have had coats which, like fur and feathers, kept heat from being lost. There is a strong hint of this in fossils that show imprints of slender, hairlike scales.

Birds with Teeth

When Jurassic pterosaurs died and sank into lagoons, they shared their burial places with some of the world's oldest birds. Their fossils include imprints of feathers as well as a petrified skull, teeth, and bones.

These birds, called *Archaeopteryx*, were almost as large as crows. The head was large, the neck was long, and the body was balanced on legs that ended in feet with three clawed toes that pointed forward and one short toe behind. Besides being about as large as a crow, *Archaeopteryx* apparently walked like one.

Mouth, wings, and tail, however, showed that *Archaeopteryx* was closely related to reptiles. The jaws contained teeth and were covered with scales, the wings had three clawed toes, and the tail took up about half of the whole vertebral column. A row of feathers grew along each side of the tail, and similar feathers extended onto the toes on each wing. Though *Archaeopteryx* undoubtedly flew, the lack of a deeply keeled breastbone showed that the wing muscles were too weak for swift, long-sustained flight.

Having taken to air, birds adapted themselves to life above, on, and in salt water. Late Cretaceous seas in which mosasaurs abounded furnished fish for birds that must have looked and acted like plump terns. They had shortened their tails and lengthened their skulls, and had covered their jaws with sharp bills instead of the scales of *Archaeopteryx*. Long bones were hollow, reducing weight; hipbones

Skull

Archæopteryx, a very primitive bird, lived on islands in a Jurassic sea that covered central Europe.

were fused into one strong structure; the breastbone bore a deep keel to which muscles that moved the wings were attached. Only teeth, which still grew from the jaws, showed that these birds belonged to a group that still was primitive.

While these toothed birds were turning into strong flyers, one of their relatives became almost as firmly tied to water as its neighbors, the mosasaurs.

Hesperornis ("western bird") measured about 4 feet from his beak to the tip of his short tail. His long body was torpedo-shaped; his wings were mere remnants, and his legs were placed so far to the rear that they were fit only for swimming. At the surface they served as oars; below it, they drove *Hesperornis* forward in power dives to capture belemnoids and fish or to escape hungry reptiles.

Was success the reward of this specialization? Only for a few million years. *Hesperornis* appeared in Late Cretaceous seas, prospered briefly in spite of savage fish and carnivorous reptiles, and apparently died out long before the period came to an end. But birds of other types lived on, and most of them retained their wings. These organs reach their greatest development in the modern wandering albatross, which has a wingspread of 11 feet 8 inches or more. One of the largest flying birds was an Ice-age vulture that tore meat from elephants mired in the tar pits of southern California. These scavengers had wings 12 or more feet wide and weighed about 50 pounds, or twice as much as a modern condor.

Flightless Giants

Though birds possess the world's most efficient wings, they have repeatedly abandoned the air in favor of flightless life on the ground. This first occurred in Eocene times, when a thick-legged bird 7 feet tall roamed prairies in Wyoming. It happened again in the Miocene

Hesperornis, the toothed diving bird, could neither fly nor walk.

Epoch, when a bird 5 feet in height hunted mammals in South America. Another South American predator was even larger, for its drumstick alone was 30 inches long.

Even this creature seems small when we compare it with plant-eaters that lived in Madagascar and New Zealand until a few centuries ago. *Aepyornis* ("tall bird") of Madagascar was 7 to 8 feet in height and weighed about 1000 pounds; some moas of New Zealand weighed only half as much but were more than 10 feet tall. Both *Aepyornis* and moas reached their zenith during the Ice Age but survived into the Recent Epoch and were eaten by early man.

14 WARM BLOOD AND HAIR

WHILE BIG DINOSAURS splashed through swamps near Bone Cabin, some very different animals hid in the forests, waiting for a chance to become important. Their descendants kept on waiting through seventy-odd million years of Cretaceous time, until the Mesozoic Era ended. Then they became common and so varied that we often describe the Cenozoic as the Era of Mammals.

Our language, of course, is figurative; no animal ever knowingly waited for a chance to become anything. Still, mammals did hide in Morrison forests, and they lived on through the Cretaceous Period without becoming common or big enough to threaten even the smallest dinosaurs. Then, after long and—to us—dreary stagnation, they became the most progressive and aggressive animals to be found on

Lycaenops, Late Permian

Cynognathus, of Early Triassic age

Two reptiles that were evolving into mammals. Both lived in South Africa.

land. Before two epochs passed, they also took up marine life by evolving into whales.

But what, precisely, are mammals?

They are creatures which the British term "beasts"; we often call them "animals" in a tone that sets them apart from birds, reptiles, amphibians, fish, and the great host of invertebrates. Fossil mammals must be recognized by peculiarities of teeth, skulls, and skeletons. These characteristics are shared by living mammals, which we may define very briefly as vertebrates that have warm blood and hair. No other living creature has either, but every present-day mammal has both, even though porpoises and whales retain very little hair.

Two types of living mammals lay eggs, but the young of other types are born. All young mammals start out by drinking milk which comes from glands in the mother's skin. Indeed, the word "mammal" literally means an animal that has mammae, or milk glands. Some persons prefer this definition to the one that relies on warm blood and hair as distinctive characters.

From Reptiles to Mammals

We often speak of "missing links" between different groups of animals. The term comes from early days of the study of evolution, when the fossil ancestors of most animal groups had not yet been discovered. Today, however, many "missing" links have been found. Some, indeed, have become series of links which trace the steps by which animals of one type changed into something else.

This is true of the no-longer-missing links between reptiles and mammals. They first appeared in South Africa during Late Permian times, when reptiles related to *Varanosaurus* and *Dimetrodon* developed superficially doglike skulls and teeth of four types: small, sharp nippers in front, large "eyeteeth" or canines, pointed teeth of ordinary size, and three-pronged cutters far back on the jaws. There is a clear resemblance between these teeth and those of modern mammals such as opossums. Some of these reptiles also kept their legs close to the body, raising it well above the ground. The legs themselves were fitted for rapid walking and running, in contrast to the sprawling gait of such reptiles as *Varanosaurus*.

The gap between these creatures and mammals was narrow; it was further reduced by Triassic reptiles that lost some reptilian bones from the skull and all but lost others in the jaw. Though their fossils

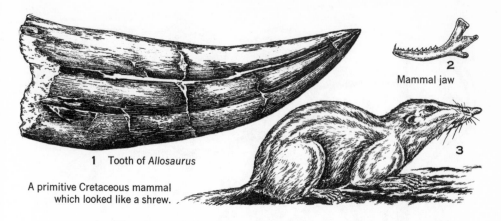

1   Tooth of *Allosaurus*

2
Mammal jaw

3

A primitive Cretaceous mammal
which looked like a shrew.

One tooth of *Allosaurus* (1) was four times as long as the entire jaw of a Jurassic mammal (2) and as long as this Cretaceous species (3).

lack skin and flesh, we assume that their scales were turning into hairs while their hearts were developing the structure that keeps the blood of mammals warm. These changes probably were accomplished during Triassic times.

Mammals of the Mesozoic

Mammal-like reptiles of the Late Permian were 4 to 8 feet in length; Triassic types were smaller, and early mammals were smaller still. Those that lived in the Morrison forests were seldom larger than mice or rats. The few that equaled woodchucks in size were the giants of their kind and time.

The contrast between these little creatures and big dinosaurs is most impressive. One museum has dramatized it by placing an allosaur tooth beside an entire mammalian jaw found in the same quarry on Como Bluff, Wyoming, a few miles south of Bone Cabin. The tooth—just one of 70 or more—is a sharp-pointed weapon 6 inches long with finely serrate edges. The jaw measures 1.5 inches over-all; its teeth, though sharp, would kill nothing much bigger than a cockroach. How could their owner do more than eat, mate, and keep out of carnivorous reptiles' sight?

In one respect this exhibit is deceptive; no allosaur ever bothered to kill and eat small mammals. But that big tooth does not represent

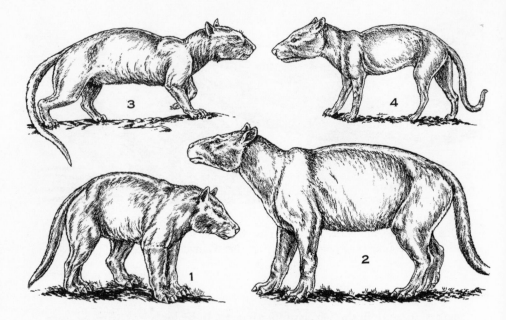

Four Early Tertiary mammals. Number 1, a Paleocene herbivore that probably ate meat as well as plants. Number 2, the Early Eocene herbivore *Phenacodus*. Numbers 3 and 4, two Early Eocene carnivores.

Allosaurus alone; it stands for the whole array of meat-eating reptiles that must have lived in Jurassic forests. Some of them did devour mouse- and rat-sized creatures; others were ready to snap up any mammal that became large enough to attract their attention. Since an animal that was eaten produced no young ones, selection kept early mammals small while the Jurassic Period came to an end and throughout Cretaceous times.

The Cretaceous Period, like the Permian, was brought to an end by such great changes that we call them an earth-revolution. The Rocky Mountains and Andes were bent, broken, and thrust upward, volcanoes erupted in many places, and enormous masses of molten rock filled the cores of other mountains. Climates became cooler than they had been, and the last dinosaurs died out. With them vanished most of the reptiles that had preyed upon little Cretaceous mammals. Their descendants at last were free to grow without being eaten because they did so.

Triumphs in a Changed World

The first results of this new freedom were hardly spectacular Many mammals of the earliest Cenozoic Epoch were small; those that were not were clumsy creatures with blunt heads, heavy legs, and five-toed feet. Some types were technically carnivores, yet their claws were very nearly hoofs and their teeth show that they often ate plants. Hoofed mammals, which should have been plant-eaters, also were omnivorous. Some did become good-sized, for one kind was larger than a sheep, and another reached 8 feet in length.

Eocene mammals became larger and stronger than more ancient types, but remained unintelligent and clumsy. Some kinds, such as *Phenacodus*, also combined contrasting features. When the teeth of this creature were discovered, they suggested that their owner was piglike, but when skeletons were unearthed they revealed long-tailed animals as small as a fox or larger than a goat. All had arched backs, five-toed feet, and hoofs that still were almost claws. From a distance, the beasts must have resembled big cats that had traded heads with sheep but followed the feeding habits of swine. An ancient Greek philosopher imagined that animals began when separate parts that had been moving about came together hit-or-miss. He, would have found *Phenacodus* a fine example of his theory.

These apparent misfits were normal, however, and they surely were not imaginary. They also provided carnivores called creodonts with generous amounts of food. Some of those carnivores resembled short-legged wolves; others were crudely catlike; one group resembled hyenas. Actually, neither cats, wolves, nor hyenas existed during the Eocene Epoch.

Since Late Triassic times most mammals had been small; then, during the Eocene Epoch, plant-eaters produced their earliest giants. One was a barrel-bodied beast 8 feet in length that weighed 750 to 1000 pounds. When restored, it suggests a pigmy hippopotamus with swollen legs and an elephant's feet, but its canine teeth were long, sharp tusks. The creature probably lived in swamps.

Uintatheres were named for the Uinta Basin of Utah and Colorado, in which they were discovered. Early species were piglike in size but not in appearance, for they had flat heads and very deep lower jaws. *Uintatherium* itself, of Middle Eocene age, stood 5 feet high, had six blunt, skin-covered "horns," and fought with canine tusks 7 inches in length. In Late Eocene times, the giant of the family stood 7 feet high at the shoulder, had a skull 40 inches long, and his tusks extended 9 inches below the upper jaw. The beast weighed 4 to 5 tons.

The biggest Eocene carnivore lived in Mongolia. Its skull was 34 inches long—a grizzly bear's skull measures 18 or 19 inches. If other dimensions were in proportion, the Eocene meat-eater was some 12 feet long and 7 feet high.

Cavities which held their brains show that these early giants were dull-witted. Though the largest uintathere was as heavy as most elephants, his brain was smaller and less efficient than that of a 3000-pound rhinoceros. He must have lived largely by instinct and simple reflex, for conscious thought was a luxury in which he could hardly indulge.

That may not have been a disadvantage, for the big uintathere had few associates that were much brighter than he was. It is true that

The largest uintathere stood 7 feet high at the shoulder, and its six-horned skull was 40 inches long.

both they and he died out at the end of Eocene times—but not until uintatheres had grown bigger and bigger through about 20 million years. Few estimates credit mankind with more than 800,000 years of existence, and already we are threatening ourselves with catastrophic destruction. Did the uintathere really do badly with his oversized body and undersized brain?

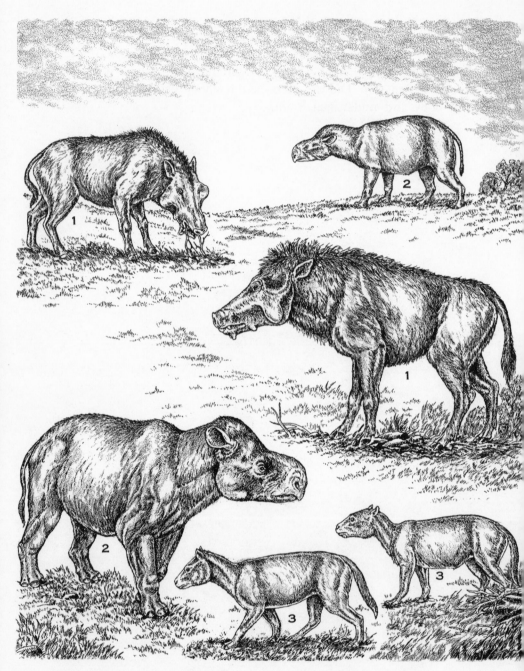

Three mammals of the White River Badlands. Number 1, giant pig. Number 2, hornless rhinoceros. Number 3, *Oreodon*, a small herbivore.

15 BEASTS OF BADLANDS AND RANCHES

MANY TOURISTS bound for Yellowstone National Park turn southward at a junction west of Kadoka, South Dakota. For hours they have crossed rolling plains, but soon their road skirts cream-colored cliffs and then descends into the maze of ridges, pinnacles, flats, and narrow canyons that make up the Big, or White River, Badlands.

To old-time Indians this region was *Mako Sika:* bad country in which to travel or hunt. French traders translated the name as *Mauvaises Terres;* English-speaking pioneers turned it into *Badlands.* General Custer, always flamboyant, described the region as "part of Hell with the fires burned out."

Paved roads now make travel easy through the Badlands; a campground and lodge provide for tourists who remain overnight in order to see the country at its best. Before sunset and in the morning, Custer's inferno is a photographer's paradise.

Here fossil hunters agree with shutterbugs, for these delicately tinted buttes and ridges are famous for their petrified mammal bones. Most of them date from the Oligocene Epoch, when the northern Great Plains were level prairies with groves, ponds and swampy lakes, and rivers that often overflowed. Volcanoes far to the westward erupted cloud upon cloud of pale volcanic ash that drifted over the prairies. When the ash sank to the ground it mixed with dust and with mud that had been deposited by floodwaters of streams.

Fish and several species of turtles swam in Early Oligocene rivers; plump, short-legged rhinos took mud baths in ponds. But the chief wealth of animal life was concentrated on the prairies. There herds of three-toed horses browsed, the best-known species standing less than three fourths as high as a modern pointer dog. Hornless rhinos were not much larger; small herbivores ranged in herds that avoided doglike and catlike carnivores and others that suggested small hyenas.

So-called giant pigs were plentiful but were not yet giants; they were ugly beasts 3 to 4 feet high with bony knobs on their lower jaws and broad flanges on their cheeks. Like true pigs, they rooted for food, and gritty dirt that clung to roots wore grooves in their teeth.

The real giants of early White River prairies belonged to a family appropriately named titanotheres. Several of its members stood 6 to 8 feet high, were 10 to 14 feet long, and weighed 3 to 5 tons. The largest species suggested a massive rhinoceros with a low, concave head and two blunt horns side by side on the nose. Those horns, which really were bony projections covered with skin, were much larger in males than in females. Bull titanotheres probably battered one another with them during the mating season.

Not all titanotheres were giants, however, and several kinds did not have large horns. The earliest members of the group, which lived

A scene in the White River Badlands of South Dakota

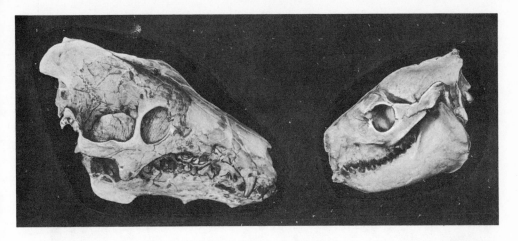

Skull of a young giant pig (left) and a small oreodont (right). Both skulls, from the White River Badlands of South Dakota, are in the museum of Princeton University.

in the West during Early Eocene times, were smaller than modern sheep; instead of horns they had only a bony knob above each eye. As time passed the knobs moved forward while the head and body inceased in size and the legs became massive columns that ended in short-toed feet. A Late Eocene titanothere stood 4 feet high at the shoulder, or a foot less than a rhinoceros weighing about 3000 pounds. An Early Oligocene species was only 4 inches taller but approached a rhinoceros in weight. Huge, heavy-horned titanotheres came later, near the end of Early Oligocene times. With these giants, however, lived smaller species whose horns remained short.

Titanotheres, like rhinos, were browsers. Those of moderate size got their food from bushes, but big ones pulled leaves and twigs from low trees. The animals must have done this with long, muscular lips, for their front teeth were small or had disappeared. Their back teeth had become big crushers and grinders which were much wider on the upper jaws than they were below.

What Killed the Titanotheres?

We have mentioned only American titanotheres, but the family also ranged across Asia and into eastern Europe. They prospered from Late Eocene through Early Oligocene times—a span of 15 or 18 million years. This was enough, we might think, to establish the beasts as solid mammalian citizens with an important future. Instead, they

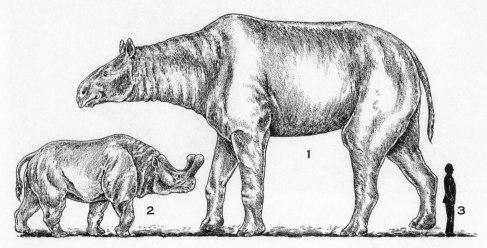

Giant hornless rhinoceros of Asia (1), compared with a big titanothere (2), and a 6-foot man (3).

became extinct in the Old World as well as the New. Throughout Middle and Late Oligocene times, giant pigs and hornless rhinos were the largest animals that lived on the White River prairies and in other parts of the West.

What caused this seemingly sudden extinction? Why did the titanotheres die out soon after many species had become big, powerful, and well armed?

One theory says that big titanotheres could not find and eat enough food to nourish their massive bodies. The hungry giants became weak and unhealthy, falling prey to enemies and diseases or starving when smaller and more active beasts such as rhinos ate the available food. This theory finds its support in the fact that the mouths and teeth of titanotheres did not increase in size as rapidly as their bodies. Still, the lag does not seem great enough to have caused widespread starvation. And what about species that died out although they remained small?

Another theory says that titanotheres were too stupid to compete with new animals that had bigger and better brains. We must grant that big titanotheres were dull; species that weighed 4 or 5 tons had brains no larger than those of 1500-pound rhinos. Still, new mammals that appeared in the Middle Oligocene possessed brains that

A slab of rhinoceros skulls and bones from the Agate Springs deposit, north-west of Gering, Nebraska. *American Museum of Natural History*

were not much better than those of earlier creatures. Why should the new beasts defeat much stronger titanotheres in the struggle for homes and food?

A third theory holds that titanotheres were killed by new diseases spread by insects such as tsetse flies. This, however, is speculation that lacks supporting evidence.

A fourth explanation seeks to improve upon and support the first. Big titanotheres, it reminds us, needed almost as much food as a modern elephant requires. That food, however, had to be soft, for titanothere teeth were so poorly constructed that they could not with-stand much wear. Any change that brought in harsher, tougher plants than those to which the big beasts were adapted would have led to starvation as teeth were worn down to the gums.

This theory is more attractive than any other, especially if we hold that the effort to get food was hampered by dull brains. But how critical was that dullness, and did tender plants give way to coarse ones on a scale that could drive *all* titanotheres to extinction at the end of Early Oligocene times? Moreover, were the titanotheres' teeth much less durable than those of the modern rhinoceros, which lives in a world of dry, harsh plants? Until these questions are answered the theory will remain unproved.

An Asiatic Giant

Though some titanotheres weighed as much as elephants, they were not the largest Oligocene mammals. That distinction belongs to a hornless rhinoceros that appeared in Asia and lived on into the Miocene Epoch. The bones first came to light in 1911, in what now is western Pakistan. They were named *Baluchitherium* ("Beast of Baluchistan") by a British scientist who hoped that future discoveries would tell more about the creatures.

This hope was fulfilled in 1922 by Walter Granger, who had discovered Bone Cabin 25 years before. In Mongolia Granger unearthed remains of three baluchitheres, one of which included 365 fragments of a shattered skull. When the remains reached New York City, a skilled preparator took three months to assemble the skull while other men worked on bones of the legs and body. In the end, the fossils revealed an animal with a head almost 5 feet long, a 6-foot neck, a body 16 feet in length, and a height of 18 feet at the shoulder. These dimensions made *Baluchitherium* the largest known land-dwelling mammal. He did not, of course, rival the dimensions and bulk of *Brachiosaurus*, *Apatosaurus*, or many lesser dinosaurs. Like them, however, *Baluchitherium* seems to have been a peaceful herbivore whose safety lay in his great size.

Animals of Agate Springs Ranch

The Agate Springs Ranch lies in Sioux County, Nebraska, about 100 airline miles from the Big Badlands. By road the distance is much greater, but this figure ceases to impress us when we turn miles into geologic time. If we start from the Titanothere Beds, near the center of the Badlands, our trip spans 12 million years and transports us into the Early Miocene world.

The first mammals that demand our attention are calf-sized rhinoceroses with two short horns side by side on their noses. These animals must have run in great herds, for the remains of 16,500 individuals lie in a single small hill east of the Agate Springs ranch-

Mammals of the Agate Springs deposit. Number 1, two-horned rhinoceros. Number 2, giant pig. Number 3, *Moropus*, a plant-eater with claws.

house. All these bones and skulls are crowded into one bed of fine-grained sandstone 6 to 20 inches in thickness.

This bed is more puzzling than its fossils. It has been called an ancient quicksand in which mammals were mired while they drank. It may represent an eddy in which dead bodies came to rest and were covered with sand. The sand may also have formed a river bar on which carcasses were stranded. But why were they torn to pieces, so that only skulls and separate bones are found? Why are there no skeletons or even articulated leg bones?

Among the horde of rhinoceros bones are those of two larger beasts. One of them, called *Moropus*, was a plant-eater as tall as a modern camel, but with shorter, thicker neck and legs. So far as we know, there was no hump; the feet bore huge claws instead of the

Small American camels. Number 1 is an Oligocene species from the White River Badlands. Number 2 is the Miocene camel whose bedding ground was on the Agate Springs Ranch.

hoofs we expect to find on a plant-eater. Perhaps the claws were used for digging roots and for defense. A blow from one of *Moropus'* forefeet would have staggered any enemy.

What enemy? Probably not a carnivore, for flesh-eaters of the Early Miocene were neither large nor very common. The most likely troublemaker was *Dinohyus*, a giant pig that stood 7 feet high at the shoulder, with a long head and teeth that were almost wolflike. They suggest that the beast was a savage fighter, both with his own kind and with other mammals.

Another hill on the Agate Springs Ranch seems to have been the bedding ground of humpless camels 2 feet high that resembled antelopes and had sharp hoofs instead of pads on their feet. These creatures traveled in herds, feeding during the day and resting in special places at night. Old animals and sick ones died while they slept, and winds soon covered them with sand. Their bones now lie in skeletons, not in the closely packed disorder of the rhinoceros remains.

Members of the camel family went on changing, and for millions of years left their remains in various parts of the West. One group, called giraffe-camels because of their appearance, developed long necks and legs and reached heights of 8 to 16 feet at the top of the head, not the shoulders. They probably stalked across western plains as true giraffes stalk over those of Africa today, eating leaves and twigs of trees.

During most of Miocene and Early Pliocene times, the main line of camel evolution was embodied in humpless animals about 4

A pair of early giraffe-camels called *Oxydactylus*; they were 4 feet 6 inches high at the shoulder. Some species grew as tall as present-day giraffes.

feet high at the shoulder. In time, some of their descendants reached South America and became guanacos, the wild ancestors of llamas. Meanwhile, others became true camels, though it is not clear whether they did so before or soon after they wandered into Asia. Still others became animals larger than modern dromedaries, though they may not have possessed humps. These creatures lived through the Ice Age and into modern times. Their last survivors may have died no more than 5000 years ago.

16 PATHS TO PROMISED LANDS

WHEN HERNANDO CORTEZ set out to conquer Mexico, in 1518, he took more than six hundred foot soldiers and eighteen horsemen, as well as several cannons. The noise of guns terrified the Indians, the Spaniards themselves appeared to be immortal, and the horsemen led savage attacks. Even the horses themselves appeared as angry representatives of the Spanish king, ready to destroy anyone who disobeyed Cortez' orders.

We already know that these animals were not the first members of their family in North America. Little three-toed horses roamed the White River prairies, and larger three-toed species followed during the Miocene Epoch. Later came one-toed species which spread to South America and the Old World. In the latter they still survive as horses, zebras, and asses, though their last American relatives died out 8,000 to 10,000 years ago.

Is this history of horses unique? Or have other groups of animals also begun in one region and spread into others, where they lived and prospered long after they had become extinct in their original homes?

Though horses are well-known travelers, they are not unusual. Since Precambrian times animals, plants, and other creatures have been evolving, spreading through seas or across new lands, and dying out where they once were common. When horses did these things they merely followed the crowd.

We often say that animals migrate from region to region or from one continent to another on which they have not lived before. We do not refer, however, to seasonal journeys like those made by birds in spring and autumn or by fur seals in the Pacific Ocean. We also do not mean irresistible mass movements such as those that force millions of lemmings overland until they plunge into the ocean and drown.

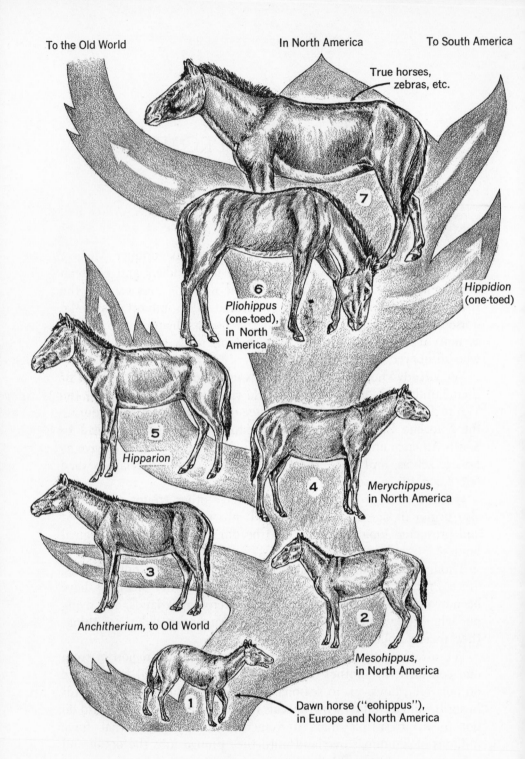

To the Old World   In North America   To South America

True horses, zebras, etc.

7

Hippidion (one-toed)

6
Pliohippus (one-toed), in North America

5
Hipparion

4
Merychippus, in North America

3
Anchitherium, to Old World

2
Mesohippus, in North America

1
Dawn horse ("eohippus"), in Europe and North America

Important stages in the evolution of horses and their travels

Such trips are spectacular, but in the end they leave species and larger groups just where they were before. Migrations that have taken animals to new parts of the world are less conspicuous. Most of them began when herds, families, or even single creatures wandered off to find food, shelter, mates, or whatnot and *did not return to their original homes.* Few trips of this sort were very long; a mile was a great distance to a rabbit or a land-dwelling beaver, and most three-toed horses beset by wanderlust may have stopped before they were 30 miles from the glades in which they were foaled. But they stopped where they were at the end of each trip, and in time some of them or their offspring went 20 to 30 miles farther still. Repetition without return, not the length of each trip, led to enduring results.

Avenues, Barriers, Bridges

This, therefore, is the sort of travel we mean when we say that living things migrated, or spread, from one part of the world to another. The method was slow, variable, and often unsure, for travelers were free to delay, zigzag, or change their course whenever they felt like doing so. Migrants might also be stopped by barriers which they could not cross. Land of any sort was a barrier to marine creatures; those that traveled on land might be halted by deserts, mountain systems, and by seas. On the other hand, land migrants might be helped by broad avenues of easily traveled country or by bridges of narrow land that arose between continents.

Both a bridge and a broad avenue for migration figured in the story of horses. Like camels, they seem to be native Americans, though some of their earliest members lived in Europe as well as the West during the Eocene Epoch. The European animals produced some oversized, tapir-shaped descendants and then died out, leaving the evolutionary future to the American branch of their family.

We already know that many Eocene mammals were small, stupid, and unspecialized, and the varied species of dawn horse, or eohippus, were not exceptions to this rule. All had four toes in front and three behind, but some were 18 inches high at the shoulder and others were only 10.

From these beginnings came animals that grew more and more horselike. We have seen the small, graceful *Mesohippus* of Oligocene times, which was followed by larger Miocene types which also had

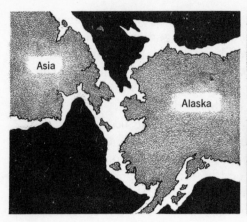

Two important land bridges. At the left is the Bering bridge (white) as it would be if sea level were to sink 150 feet, or about half the amount land has risen since the Ice Age. At the right is the Central American bridge, broken into three islands during a period when the land sank or the sea level rose. Any of these gaps would prevent large mammals from going from one American continent to the other.

three toes. One of the latter was a restless migrant that spread northward over rolling prairies which provided a broad avenue of travel across the West, Canada, and Alaska.

Any mammal that crosses Alaska today comes to a salt-water barrier in the form of the Bering Sea and Strait. Many ancient mammals were met by that barrier, too, but the wandering three-toed horses were not. Two or three million years before they arrived, the bottom of Bering Strait became a rolling plain that extended from Alaska to Siberia. In geologic terms, it formed a land bridge between North America and Asia. Horses casually wandered over that bridge and then spread across Asia and through much of Europe.

North America was not abandoned, however, and animals that remained in their homeland continued to produce offspring that differed from their parents. The result was several groups of horses that still had three toes on each foot, though only one toe was big enough to be useful. Members of the group now called *Hipparion* were as large as a modern "light" cow pony and ate grass instead of browsing. Hipparions also crossed the Bering land bridge in Early Pliocene times and continued westward. So far as we know, they were the first horses to reach Africa.

Stay-at-homes kept on evolving—this time into one-toed horses. They began with *Pliohippus*, a lightly built animal that apparently gave rise to zebras, true horses, and asses or donkeys. Zebras were the first of these to cross the land bridge; they reached Europe early in the Pleistocene Ice Age but took many more years to reach Africa. By the time they did so, other members of the family had established themselves on every continent except Australia and Antarctica.

Horses remained common in the Americas throughout the Ice Age; though some were ponies only 40 inches high, others were as big as the modern Belgian draft horse, which stands 5 feet high at the shoulder and weighs as much as a ton. Then, as the Pleistocene Epoch ended, American horses rapidly died out. As we know, not a single native species remained when Spanish conquerors brought chargers from Europe.

Animal Immigrants

To Americans, horses appear as emigrants, since they spread northward across the Bering land bridge and went on into other continents. True camels were emigrants, too, but many animals took the route in reverse. Starting from Asia, Europe, or even Africa, they crossed the land bridge and came as immigrants to what for them was a truly new world. Horned dinosaurs seem to have taken this course; very ancient mammals surely did so. Rhinos were immigrants to North America too, and so were the ancestors of our "big game" animals—bison, moose, elk, deer, pronghorn—as well as most of the carnivores that once preyed upon them.

In distance traveled, the proboscideans, or elephants and their kin, rank high among migrants. They began in northern Africa during the Eocene Epoch, in the form of heavily built animals about as large as modern pigs or tapirs. After spreading into Europe and across Asia, some of their descendants wandered over the Bering land bridge. Thus they began a series of invasions that continued through 15 to 20 million years and encompassed both North and South America.

The first proboscideans to cross the Bering land bridge were beasts about 5 feet high at the shoulder, with very long upper jaws and short tusks both above and below. After them came other long-jawed beasts, followed by still others with short lower jaws and long, elephantine tusks above. Their best-known member, the American mastodon, may have evolved in Asia but became most abundant in the New World and died out only a few thousand years ago. It stood 7 to 9 feet high at the shoulder and was covered with shaggy hair.

While mastodons were evolving and spreading, some of their relatives became the elephants called mammoths. They, too, crossed the Bering land bridge, in a variety of species that ranged from long-haired animals not much larger than American mastodons to giants whose skins were probably bare and whose height at the shoulder reached 14 feet. The long-haired species was killed and eaten by ancient men of Europe, but bare-skinned animals called southern or Columbian mammoths were favored game in the Southwest and in Mexico some 10,000 to 11,000 years ago.

Across the Isthmus

Although other routes have been suggested, the Bering land bridge is the only one by which land mammals are known to have traveled from the Old-world continents of Africa, Europe, and Asia into North America. Another bridge was needed, however, to let them continue their journey to South America or to leave it and migrate northward again.

We sometimes think of this second bridge as the Isthmus of Panama. Actually it extends from southern Mexico through Central America to northern Colombia—an airline distance of 1470 miles, of which the Isthmus makes up only 130. Since large portions of this bridge were submerged during almost 50 million years of the Cenozoic Era, it serves as an excellent example of both an avenue for migration and a barrier to it.

The whole Central American bridge was above water during the Paleocene Epoch and part of the Eocene. These, as we know, were times when many mammals remained small and weak, and when the few that grew to large size were stupid, clumsy, and slow. Probably because they were, they did not reach the land bridge, where travelers were limited to opossumlike beasts, ancestors of sloths and armadillos, and a variety of ambiguous creatures that were not quite hoofed herbivores but lacked claws and were not committed to a diet of meat. When parts of the land bridge sank, in Middle Eocene times, salt water barred the spread of less primitive mammals from prairies far to the north and other kinds that had come from Asia. For 50 million years, beasts that had reached and crossed the Isthmus

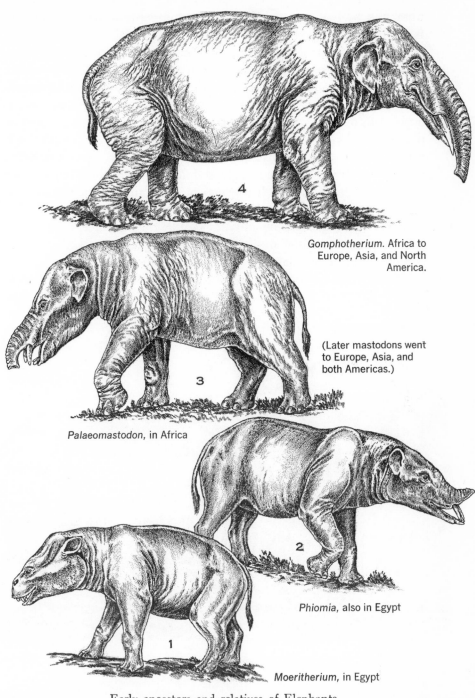

Gomphotherium. Africa to Europe, Asia, and North America.

(Later mastodons went to Europe, Asia, and both Americas.)

Palaeomastodon, in Africa

Phiomia, also in Egypt

Moeritherium, in Egypt

Early ancestors and relatives of Elephants

were free to live and evolve without competition from more able types that developed in other parts of the world.

Isolation can have bizarre results; in South America it led to an outburst of creatures which were both primitive and highly specialized. Some marsupials, for instance, became opossums, which means that they carried on the ways and forms of their ancestors. Others evolved into meat-eaters that superficially resembled ferrets, wolves, pumas, and even saber-tooth cats. Some armadillos remained small, others became as big as oxen, and a few kinds must have weighed 2 tons. Their close relatives, the glyptodonts, covered their bodies with thick, bony shells, and built up rings of bone around their tails. One group even covered much of the tail with a bony tube that ended in a cluster of spikes. Strong muscles swung this clublike organ from side to side when one of these glyptodonts was attacked.

Sloths, too, were related to armadillos; in forests, one group hung upside down in trees, moving so little and so slowly that they hardly seemed to be alive. In open country, other sloths stayed on the

Macrauchenia (left) and *Toxodon* (right), two bizarre beasts that evolved in South America but died out after the Central American land bridge was re-established. *Toxodon* weighed some 5000 pounds.

ground, where they became massive animals 7 to 20 feet long. They walked clumsily on the sides of their feet and their knuckles, and were armed with massive claws.

Some plant-eaters became small, graceful beasts with feet more horselike than those of the horses which then lived in North America. Others became massive beasts that were 12 feet long and almost 5 feet high at the shoulder, weighed about 5000 pounds, and probably lived like the modern hippopotamus. Still stranger was a beast with thick legs, a camel-like body and neck, and a short trunk. In spite of its looks, it was not related to either camels or elephants.

The land bridge rose again near the end of Pliocene times, and northern mammals soon wandered into South America. True plains-dwellers did not make the trip; they probably could not stand the humid heat of low stretches or dense forests in valleys among the mountains. Migrants did include saber-tooth cats, jaguars, wolves, horses of several kinds, tapirs, mastodons (but not mammoths), and humpless camels whose descendants are now wild guanacos and domestic llamas and alpacas.

As these creatures wandered southward they must have met South American mammals going in the opposite direction. Foremost among them were ground sloths, both the 20-foot giants and species only 7 to 8 feet long. Glyptodonts plodded northward, too, sitting close to the ground with their heads pulled in as soon as danger threatened. Armadillos rolled into balls, much as trilobites had done millions of years before. Though these animals were very different, their modes of defense were alike.

The largest ground sloths traveled as far as North Carolina; smaller species ranged westward to northern California and eastward to Florida. Glyptodonts and armadillos stayed in the South, where they mingled with native species and others from the Old World. The latter included such familiar "American" animals as the bison, as well as mastodons and mammoths. The last two, like the glyptodonts and ground sloths, have been extinct for several thousand years.

In life's struggle, extinction is failure but survival and increase are success. By this standard only two South American immigrants have been successful in North America. One of these is the armadillo, which has slowly spread across Texas and Louisiana into New Mexico and Mississippi and has increased its range since it was taken to peninsular Florida.

Opossums have done even better. After crossing the land bridge

Glyptodon (1), a club-tailed relative (2), and a ground sloth 18 to 20 feet long (3). All evolved in South America, but only *Glyptodon* and the ground sloth spread into North America.

they continued northward through Mexico, keeping on till they reached Illinois and the Atlantic coast before Europeans arrived. After 1600, settlers' farms and orchards furnished new supplies of food, which opossums exploited by spreading through moist, cultivated valleys. By 1927, the animals were established in southern Wisconsin and on the southern shores of Lake Ontario; by 1953 they had reached the Gulf of California in Mexico, southern Vermont in New England, South Dakota on the western prairies, and Colorado on the Great Plains. Thanks to people who took pets to the Far West and then let them escape, opossums had also become established in California, northeastern Oregon, and western Washington.

Quite a record for animals that have grown larger but are almost as sluggish, defenseless, and stupid as their ancestors were in the Eocene Epoch, some 50 million years ago!

17 APES, MAN-APES, AND APE-MEN

ONE SEPTEMBER DAY in 1924, Professor Raymond Dart was preparing to act as best man at a wedding to be held in his home in Johannesburg, South Africa. As he struggled to button a stiff wing collar, two boxes of fossil-filled rocks were delivered to his porch.

Professors are often looked upon as persons who repress unseemly enthusiasms. But Dart expected those boxes to contain baboon skulls, which are among the rarest of fossils. Throwing the collar aside, he snatched tools, opened one box—and found some battered turtle eggs. Off came the lid of the other box; in it lay a natural cast of the brain case of a young ape more manlike than any baboon or gorilla. Near the cast were bones of the face and lower jaw.

While Dart examined the fossil his wife twice begged him to finish dressing; he neither saw nor heard her. The groom-to-be became insistent, so the professor donned collar, tie, and coat and went through his part in the ceremony. As the last guests were leaving, however, Dart hurried back to the specimens. How could he remove the rock from that childlike face and jaw?

Most scientists leave such jobs to skilled preparators who work with specially designed tools. But Dart's university was young and poor, so the professor became his own technician, using tools bought at a hardware store and one of his wife's knitting needles for especially delicate work. He tapped, pried, and scraped for seventy-three days and then wrote an article that was published in the British magazine *Nature* for February 3, 1925. There Dart described his fossil as the remains of a child about four years old which was more closely related to man than to any living ape. In spite of this, he named it *Australopithecus*, which means "southern ape." Since *Australopithecus* (pronounced AUS tra lo pi THEE′ cus) was a difficult mouthful, "man-ape" was later coined as an everyday substitute.

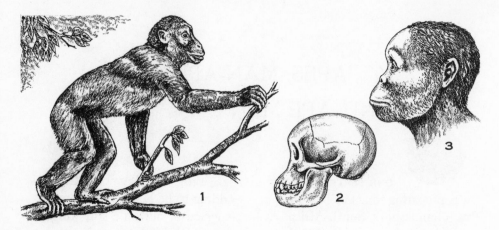

Proconsul (1), an East African ape that had characteristics pointing to man. Numbers 2 and 3 show the skull and head of Dart's original *Australopithecus* child, both restored.

From Apes to Man-apes

Professor Dart did not begin the search for "missing links," nor was *Australopithecus* the most ancient member of the series that led from Miocene mammals to man. This evolutionary patriarch was found on Rusinga Island, in Lake Victoria, and its principal discoverers were Louis S. B. and Mary Leakey. The Leakeys, we shall find, have done a great deal to unearth remains of apes, man-apes, and early men in East Africa.

In Early Miocene times Rusinga Island was part of a shallow lake into which storms washed flowers, caterpillars, slugs, and other creatures that soon sank and were petrified. The Leakeys and their co-workers also found bones and teeth of crocodiles and apes. An expert at the British Museum named the apes *Proconsul* because he mistook them for chimpanzees and because they came before—some 20 million years before—a popular chimpanzee named Consul that lived in the London Zoo.

There are three known species of *Proconsul*: one as large as a good-sized baboon, one comparable to a chimpanzee, and one as big as a modern gorilla. Most of the remains seem to have been swallowed and crushed by crocodiles, which then coughed out such resistant portions as jaws. Fortunately, one member of the baboon-sized species drowned in a water hole where mud covered him so quickly that his skull and much of his skeleton were preserved.

These remains reveal a broad-headed ape with tusklike canine teeth and a narrow muzzle. The forehead was smoothly rounded, the eye sockets were low and oblong like those of man, and there were no thick ridges of bone over the eyes. The forepart of the brain was rather monkeylike, and so were bones in the limbs. *Proconsul* apparently ran about on all fours and sometimes stood upright, but he did not swing through trees by his arms. In short, he was just the sort of animal whose descendants might change in one way and become chimpanzees and gorillas, or in another and become the ancestors of man. Some authorities think the former trend had already begun in the large species of *Proconsul*.

This can be proved only by additional skulls, or by as yet undiscovered descendants that lived during what now is a gap in our story—a gap of about 10 million years. It encompasses most of the Pliocene Epoch, during which a large part of Africa became dry grasslands and deserts, while forests grew smaller and smaller. Besides being unfavorable for most apes, these conditions kept their remains from becoming fossils and force us to fill the gap in our tale with hypothesis.

This hypothesis does have one foundation: a fragment of bone bearing four teeth which an expert African collector found in rocks of Early Pliocene age. The specimen belonged to an ape, but the teeth are more manlike than those of *Proconsul* and the bone bears impressions left by two muscles that help human beings move their lips when they talk. These impressions do not mean that the ancient apes spoke, but they do suggest that the division into gorilla-ancestors and man-ancestors had taken place before the Pliocene Epoch began.

From this starting point, our hypothesis says that some descendants of *Proconsul* developed arms of moderate length and legs long enough for walking and running. The apes we have called gorilla-ancestors, however, shortened their legs while their arms grew longer and longer. Though they became well adapted to climbing, they forced the creatures to walk on all fours when they came down to the ground.

With these differences in body went contrasting appetites. The long-armed apes preferred fruits and juicy stems, of types found only in dense, moist forests. Short-armed apes ate almost anything:

A full-grown male *Australopithecus* and two half-grown young ones. The man-like bodies and limbs contrast sharply with the apelike heads. One man-ape is selecting a bone for use as a cleaver; another holds a bone dagger; the third grasps a sharp stick and a leg-bone club.

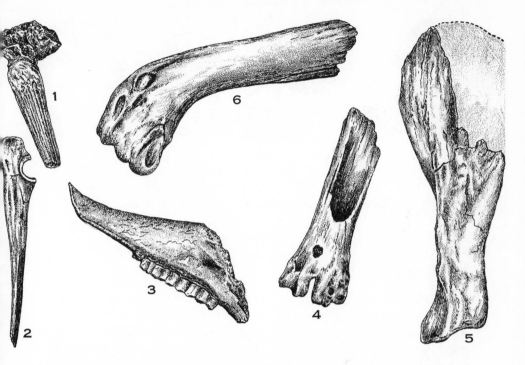

Tools of man-apes, as they are interpreted by Dart. Number 1, gazelle horn (digging tool). Number 2, split leg bone of antelope (dagger). Number 3, jaw and teeth (knife or saw). Number 4, scoop for soft food. Number 5, shoulder blade (ax or cleaver). Number 6, leg bone of antelope (club, especially useful in killing baboons).

fruits, seeds, insects, lizards, and meat which they killed or found as carrion. Such foods could be had in forests, but they also were available on dry grasslands, where apes that walked probably felt safer than they did among underbrush and trees.

Once these two trends had been established, climatic change took care of the rest. Long-armed apes went deeper and deeper into the shrinking forests, where they evolved into gorillas and chimpanzees. But as forests shrank they grew more and more crowded, and walking apes that had not already moved were pushed out to the grasslands. There, with only a few more changes, their descendants became man-apes.

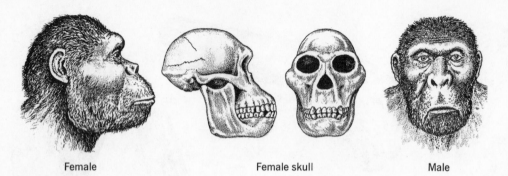

Female   Female skull   Male

Australopithecus; skull and restored heads of adults.

Two Groups of Man-apes

Before man-apes had lived very long, their descendants also evolved
into two contrasting groups. Those which Dart would someday call
Australopithecus became small, agile, quarrelsome creatures that
stood, walked, and ran in erect attitudes. Adults were 4 feet to 4
feet 6 inches tall and weighed 45 to 80 pounds, males being larger
than females. The head was small and narrow, the face and jaws
sloped forward, and the nose was almost as flat as a gorilla's. The
forehead was low, but there were no heavy ridges over the eyes.
The brain was a good deal larger than that of forest apes.

Man-apes of the second group have received several names, but
all may be called *Paranthropus*. They were 5 feet or more in height
and weighed 125 to perhaps 175 pounds. In spite of their size, their
brains were little larger than those of australopiths. Skull and face
were broad; there were thick, bony ridges above the eyes and there
was no forehead. Strong muscles ran from the lower jaw to a bony
crest on top of the skull which resembled the crest of a gorilla.
Like gorillas, *Paranthropus* apparently fed on plants that were juicy
but took a lot of chewing. This man-ape also lived in moister regions
than those favored by australopiths.

Man-apes must have appeared during the Pliocene Epoch, but
their oldest fossils have been found in rocks of the Pleistocene, or
Ice Age. For many years it was supposed that this division of earth
history began a million years ago, and the age of fossil man-apes
was set at 500,000 to 600,000 years. Then, in 1961, two scientists

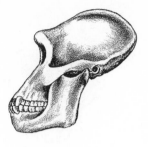

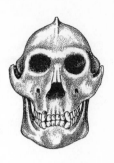

Male *Paranthropus*, the large man-ape of South Africa, showing the crest to which jaw muscles were attached.

at the University of California found that a lava flow above a skull of *Paranthropus* erupted about 1,750,000 years ago. German workers gave a lower figure but the lava they studied apparently erupted long after the other flow and therefore does not indicate its age.

Australopithecus is more ancient than *Paranthropus*; Leakey suggests that the former is as much as 2,300,000 years old. Both rocks and varied fossils found in them indicate that the little man-apes hunted on dry, grassy plains, though they often rested on rocky ridges and apparently took refuge in caves. The creatures seem to have fed on roots, seeds, insects, small mammals, and carcasses of larger beasts that had been partly eaten by leopards or lions.

Some scientists say that such carrion was the small man-apes' only source of red meat. Dart and others insist that *Australopithecus* killed antelopes, ate them, and used their leg bones as clubs to break the skulls of baboons, which also were eaten. Other bones, as well as teeth and horns, served the man-apes as daggers, cleavers, scrapers, and knives.

Dart adds that, besides killing game, small man-apes sometimes killed each other. As evidence he offers a shattered and unhealed jaw, as well as skulls broken by clubs and opened so the brains could be removed. Thus, it seems, *Australopithecus* established a practice that was followed by later ape-men and men.

Since large man-apes ate juicy plants and other foods that required moisture, *Paranthropus* did not invade southern and eastern

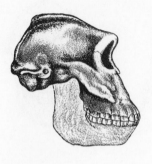

Leakey's *Zinjanthropus* (probably *Paranthropus*) from Tanzania; age about 1,750,000 years. Lower jaw restored. The crest of this man-ape is especially high.

Africa until dry climates gave way to frequent rains. Large man-apes that camped beside a lake at what is now the Olduvai Gorge, in northern Tanzania (Tanganyika), dug bulbs and roots but they also caught catfish, young crocodiles, turtles, and water birds. Bony rubbish from meals also shows that the man-apes tramped nearby grasslands in search of newborn antelopes, wild pigs, and zebras.

Though they seem to belong to the group we call *Paranthropus*, these Tanzanian man-apes were named *Zinjanthropus* by Dr. Leakey, who discovered the first massive skull. Nicknamed "Zinj," this fossil achieved world-wide fame when its age was determined as about 1,750,000 years. Near the skull were found crude tools made by chipping edges on pebbles. Zinj may or may not have chipped these tools, and local tribesmen did not believe that they were of any use. Dr. Leakey settled that question by making some pebble tools of his own. With them he skinned and cut up a sheep in less than 20 minutes.

Ape-men Were Human

Zinj, or *Paranthropus*, was as big as a man and lived like one, whether he made stone tools or did not. But we may look at Zinj's dull, heavy face without fear that we see an ancestor. If our family tree includes any man-apes they are small australopiths whose relatively large-brained descendants lived in eastern Africa even before Zinj arrived. Their homes, like the campground of Zinj himself,

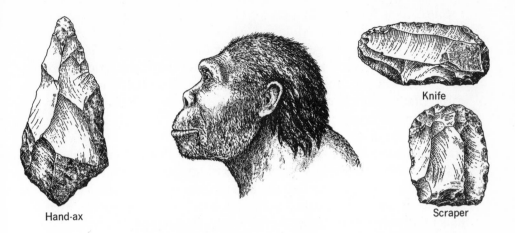

Hand-ax   Knife

                                                                Scraper

The *Pithecanthropus* of Olduvai Gorge, Tanzania, and three Abbevillian tools. This variety of ape-man had very thick ridges of bone above the eyes.

are now exposed in dry, dusty Olduvai Gorge, where Dr. Leakey and his associates have unearthed the longest record of human and almost-human life known anywhere in the world.

Leakey and his collaborators say that these Ice-age Oldowans had crossed whatever line can be drawn between man-apes and mankind and call them *Homo habilis*—"able" or "handy" man. Besides making stone tools that may include the chipped pebbles found with Zinj, these creatures apparently piled stones in circles to hold walls of brush that provided shelter from wind. The stone circles, like some fossils of the "man of ability," lie in deposits somewhat older than the stratum containing the campground where Zinj left remains of his meals.

Again some critics disagree; to them *Homo habilis* is only another type of *Australopithecus*. No one, however, doubts that Dr. Leakey has found true though primitive human beings in Olduvai Gorge. In doing so he provided an answer to the question, *Who made Chellean (or Abbevillian) tools?*

These tools were discovered in 1826, near Chelles, a few miles east of Paris. They were renamed Abbevillian for another town where specimens are both more varied and more typical. The tools are also called Chelles-Acheulian, since they form the first stage in a series named for another French town, St. Acheul.

Since their discovery in France, Chellean tools have been found in England, Spain, the Middle East, and various parts of Africa, including Olduvai Gorge. There beds some 360,000 years old contain coarsely chipped knives, scrapers and so-called axes that were held in the hand, not attached to handles, or hafts. These crude early Chellean tools are followed by better-shaped ones and then by Acheulian types.

The Leakeys discovered Olduvai's Chellean tools, and for years tried to find remains of the men who made them. Meanwhile, a French scientist working in Algeria discovered some primitive, chinless jaws in a deposit that contained hand axes and Chellean scrapers. At last, in 1960, Dr. Leakey noticed a small patch of ground that had been overlooked during earlier work. Half-buried in a bed that also contained Chellean tools lay a broken skull. When cleaned and pieced together it revealed a low, narrow forehead and brow ridges which were thicker than those of any previously known human skull. These and other characteristics convinced Dr. Leakey that his fossil was closely related to others long known as *Pithecanthropus*.

Pithecanthropus was discovered in 1890–92 by a Dutch anatomist who had become an army doctor and had gone to Java expressly to find the "missing link" between mankind and apes. To Dr. Dubois his fossils from Java were just that, so he gave them a name made from two Greek words meaning "ape" and "man." But religious leaders and many scientists disagreed. They disagreed so bitterly and so long that Dubois hid his specimens under the ground floor of his house in Holland. For years no one, not even the doctor himself, was able to examine them.

At first, Dubois thought his fossils were links between apes and men, but in his old age he called them huge gibbons. In both opinions he was mistaken. *Pithecanthropus* stood erect, had human teeth, and possessed a brain about three fourths as large as ours. In short, the creature was essentially human. Today the words *ape-man* merely translate his technical name and remind us that his low forehead, thick brow ridges, and lack of chin made his face look apelike.

Until 1927, Dubois' fossils were the only known ape-men. Then less ancient but only slightly different remains were found in a hill south of Peking, China. The Chinese ape-men took shelter in caves, cooked over fires, and chipped stones into tools which resembled those of Chellean type but were even more crude. Up to 1965, however, only the Algerian jaws and skull found by Leakey provided proof that ape-men made and used typical Chellean (or Abbevillian) tools.

Proconsul, man-apes, and African ape-men may have upset long-established ideas as to where man originated. Theorists had long maintained that mankind first appeared in central Asia, whence a succession of species or races went to other continents. Now we find that true but primitive men—the pithecanthropids—lived in Africa near the homes of their subhuman predecessors. Is it not reasonable to suppose that all evolved in central or eastern Africa, whence some of their descendants wandered to other lands?

If so, those emigrants set out at different times and traveled varying distances. Little man-apes may have gone no farther than South Africa, where most of their remains were discovered. *Pithecanthropus* then crossed Asia to China and Java, and his relatives spread through Africa, into Europe, and to the Near East.

Meanwhile, it seems, the main body of ape-men remained in East Africa. There they developed the Chellean type of tool-making, which was crude indeed when the first emigrant ape-men set off on the trip that would lead across Asia. From tools little better than those made by chipping pebbles, the stay-at-homes perfected their work through a series of styles, or stages, which the Leakeys have traced in Olduvai Gorge and at other places. Wandering ape-men took their native styles with them when they traveled, and even shared their methods with other people, some of whom were more intelligent than they. Thus men of our own species who lived in England some 300,000 years ago made Chellean hand axes, scrapers, and knives.

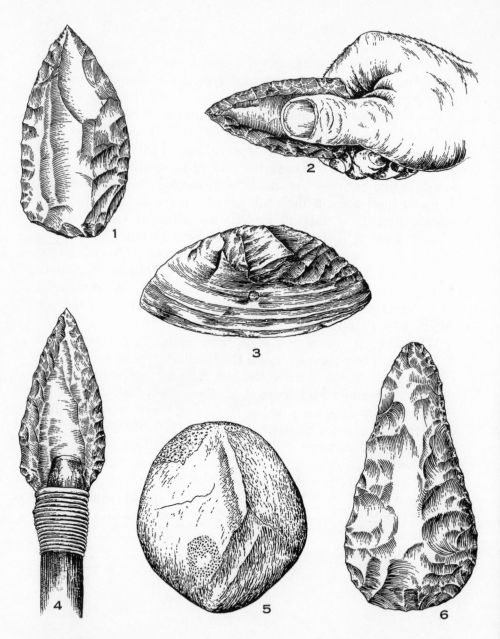

Stone tools made by Neanderthal men. Numbers 1 and 2 show an all-purpose "point," here used as a knife. Number 3 is a scraper, 4 is a spear, 5 is a hammerstone, and 6 is a small hand ax.

18 "IDIOTS" AND MAMMOTH-HUNTERS

SCIENTISTS WHO deal with human and subhuman fossils have established a record of overskepticism. First they denied that Abbevillian tools were man-made or—if they really were artifacts—insisted that they were not very old. Dubois' ape-man was then dismissed as a huge gibbon or as the skullcap of some other ape, wrongly linked to a man's thighbone. Thirty years later, several world-renowned authorities called Dart's man-ape an infant chimpanzee. Another ancient species was shrugged off as a dead Cossack soldier, a Dutchman, a feeble-minded German, or a diseased and quarrelsome idiot whose forehead had been flattened in fights. Today this "idiot" is recognized as a normal member of an exceptionally widespread and able human species known as Neanderthal man.

Quarrymen dug bones and skull of the first known Neanderthaler from a cave near Düsseldorf, Germany, in 1856. The quarry owner mistook the fossils for remains of a bear and gave them to a science teacher, who realized that they were human. He consulted a professor at Bonn, who joined him in writing an article about them. It and a lecture by the teacher started a bitter argument that raged for thirty years.

That argument wasted countless man-hours, in which learned experts showed beyond doubt that an angry, prejudiced scientist is no better than an angry, prejudiced "expert" of any other sort. Still, the battle had two good results. First, it forced supporters of the schoolmaster to present their case more convincingly than they might have done otherwise. Second, the discussion aroused so much interest that Neanderthal remains were sought and found in France, Germany, Belgium, and Czechoslovakia. Today we know that Neanderthalers ranged through the southern half of Europe and across northern Africa, the Middle East, central Asia, and China.

Though Neanderthalers were a vigorous and widespread people,

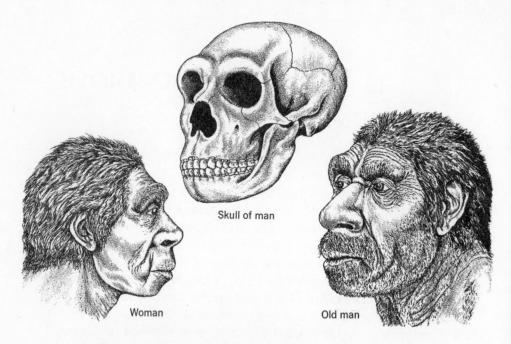

Skull of man

Woman   Old man

Neanderthalers were low-browed and had very large, thick skulls.

they were far from handsome. Men were 5 feet 2 or 3 inches tall, with big hands, short legs, and large, broad feet. The head was low, long, and larger than ours, with thick ridges over the eyes and a flattened forehead. The nose was broad and long, the jaws sloped forward, and there was no chin. Thick muscles in the neck supported the head but made the shoulders look as if they were hunched.

Such was the "classic" Neanderthaler; his wife resembled him but was a couple of inches shorter. Other races or varieties were taller, had smaller heads, or differed in other respects. Some of these variants had not reached full Neanderthal status; others may have gone beyond it. A few seem to be the results of interbreeding with more advanced but less sturdy people.

No one knows where Neanderthalers came from or just who their ancestors were. They may have evolved in Africa; they also may have arisen in Asia and traveled westward, reaching Europe 100,000 to 150,000 years ago. At that time glacial ice had all but vanished and living conditions were unusually pleasant. Large game was plentiful, for herds of reindeer lived near the remnants of glaciers, mammoths and rhinos roamed through valleys, wild cattle and horses grazed on meadows, and woods-loving deer were found in forests. Hares, ptarmigan, and moor-hens provided abundant small game.

With what weapons did Neanderthalers kill these creatures, as well as carnivores such as wolves, leopards, cave lions, and at least three kinds of bears? Hunters chipped stone into hand axes both large and small, points to be held in the hand or fastened to lances, and scrapers that also served as knives. Wooden spears were hardened by fire and rubbed to points on gritty rocks. Rhinos and mammoths were trapped in pitfalls; cave bears and lions were caught in clefts where stones could be dropped on their backs. Bears were also attacked in caverns, where at least one hunter drove a hand ax deep into his victim's skull.

Besides killing wild game, Neanderthal hunters killed and ate other Neanderthalers. Skulls were broken so brains could be removed; in this practice the face was so badly battered that for many years no one realized that the "classic" Neanderthaler had a prominent nose. Brains may have been eaten to gain the wisdom and strength of dead men, or to honor some prehistoric god. But tasty meals were important, too, and in them whole bodies were consumed. In one

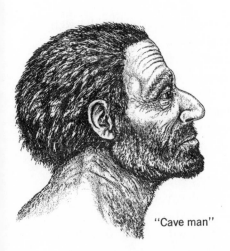
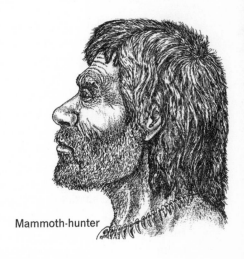

"Cave man" Mammoth-hunter

"Cave man" and mammoth-hunter. Both belonged to the modern species of man.

Yugoslavian cave, at least ten people were roasted over one fire. The broken, split bones were charred, as if the bodies had been cut to pieces and scraps were thrown onto the coals. Such a meal, in which both children and adults were eaten, does not suggest a ceremony or an offering to some god. Perhaps the feast celebrated a battle in which the victors first killed and then devoured the cave's original inhabitants.

We who can burn enemies to a crisp with nuclear bombs look upon cannibalism with horror. Yet Neanderthalers were not wholly bad, even by our biased standards. They protected their homes and got meat for their children, risking injury and death to do so. They placed honored dead in graves with weapons, food, and simple ornaments such as thin pieces of flint and ibex horns. Finally, Neanderthalers developed a religious cult of the cave bear, which apparently was sacred even though it was eaten. Cave bear skulls were stored in stone boxes or placed on bone altars built in remote ceremonial caverns. Bears' heads also were placed on poles around which cult members danced. When the men finally descended mountain trails to their homes, they doubtless believed that the animals' spirits felt highly honored, even though their bodies were ready to be cooked and eaten.

Cave Men and Mammoth-hunters

Neanderthalers prospered during the mild interglacial subepoch and lived on without much difficulty when cold, snow, and ice returned. Then, while the climate improved briefly, the low-browed hunters finally vanished. They were replaced—and absorbed—by new tribesmen whose ancestors had entered both Germany and England before Neanderthalers took over much of Europe. Like ourselves, both those ancestors and the finally-victorious tribesmen belonged to the modern human species, *Homo sapiens*, or "wise man."

In France and northern Spain, these newly dominant people camped under overhanging cliffs but painted pictures, danced, and worked magic in deep passages and rooms of caves. Their most famous personage, called the Old Man of Cro-Magnon, is often pictured as a handsome, broad-faced patriarch who stood 6 feet or more tall and was powerful in spite of his years. Modern research subtracts several inches from his height, moves him into the prime of life, and emphasizes his prominent chin, his narrow "hooked"

The woolly mammoth was well suited to life where winters were cold. *Adapted from drawing in* Prehistoric World, *by Carroll Lane Fenton, by permission of the John Day Company.*

nose, and other features that characterize present-day Caucasian peoples. Pictures painted in caverns suggest that the not-so-old man of Cro-Magnon also had fair skin and hair that was brunet or black.

Since the ancient Frenchmen were described early and dramatically, many people inferred that all Europeans of the Late Ice Age were "cave men." That some were not became evident in the 1870s when a Moravian farmer found great piles of both animal and hu-

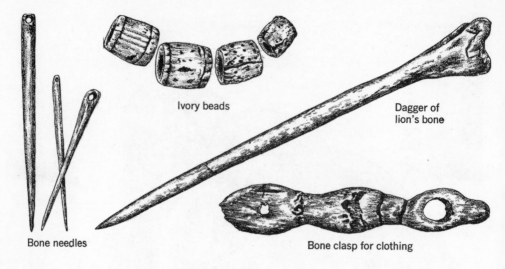

Ivory beads

Dagger of
lion's bone

Bone needles

Bone clasp for clothing

Tools and ornaments used by the mammoth-hunters of Czechoslovakia.

man bones on his land near the village of Předmostí. He ordered his laborers to crush the bones and spread them on his fields as fertilizer, a practice which he did not give up until scientists learned what was going on and persuaded the government to stop it.

By that time a great deal had been lost, but much more remained. Excavations showed that the bones had accumulated in a permanent camp built on open ground sheltered by hundred-foot cliffs of limestone. In time, remains of other camps were found in Moravia, which now is part of Czechoslovakia. Skeletons that had been buried in graves show that these ancient Czechs were sturdy though slender. The men had strong brow ridges; the jaw muscles of both sexes were thick, showing that much tough food was chewed. Thick jaw muscles forced the cheekbones to spread, making faces seem too wide for their height.

These people were sapient men, yet they did not have the wisdom to choose a pleasant habitat. They lived, instead, on open plains in a time of increasing cold, when storms that howled out of the north brought clouds of gritty dust. It settled in deposits called loess, which covered the first village until Farmer Chromatschek's men dug it away.

Rubbish piles show that game was plentiful; hunters killed cave bears, woolly rhinos, bison, musk oxen, lions, and lesser animals. In spite of this variety, the Stone-age Czechs specialized in killing the woolly mammoth, which in those days ranged from western Europe, across Asia and the Bering land bridge, and to eastern North America. As its name suggests, this mammoth was a shaggy beast with a woolly gray coat under its coarse reddish-brown hair. Unlike other mammoths, it had a prominent forehead, a hump above the shoulders, and a back that sloped steeply down to the tail. Males were 8 feet 8 inches to 9 feet 6 inches in height at the head, which was notably higher than the shoulders.

Such beasts could hardly be brought down by spears and axes; the hunters therefore dug pitfalls across mammoth trails and set up sharpened stakes in each pit. Those stakes pierced the entrails of any victim that crashed through the flimsy layer of boughs and soil that hid the pit from sight. Stone weapons then killed the mammoth, or it was left to bleed to death.

Now and then, where a sturdy tree overhung a pit, the hunters employed a big stone maul lashed to a rawhide rope. Once a mammoth was trapped, the rope was passed over a branch, and the hunters began to pull. Up, up went the maul till the leader gave a signal that meant *Let go!* and the stone crashed down upon the victim. One well-placed blow from such a maul was worth dozens of spear thrusts.

Mammoths provided the villagers with much more than food. Forks, spoons, spear points, and paint holders were carved out of tusks, some of which were 15 feet long. Ivory balls wrapped in skin became weights on bolas which were thrown to entangle the legs of horses. Ribs were shaped into ax handles; war clubs were carved from leg bones which already had massive heads. Other leg bones formed the lower walls of skin tent-houses, which were partly sunk into the ground as protection from gales and cold. Unused bones were piled into ditches, since they were too big and too abundant to be tossed on rubbish heaps.

Though mammoth bones made fine war clubs, lion bones cut down and sharpened were preferred for daggers. Other bones provided material for needles, clasps to hold skin clothing together, spadelike tools, and others that resembled forks.

Before ceremonies, priests and dancers painted themselves with colored earths which they mixed with grease on bone or ivory palettes. There were few ornaments except paint and necklaces; now and

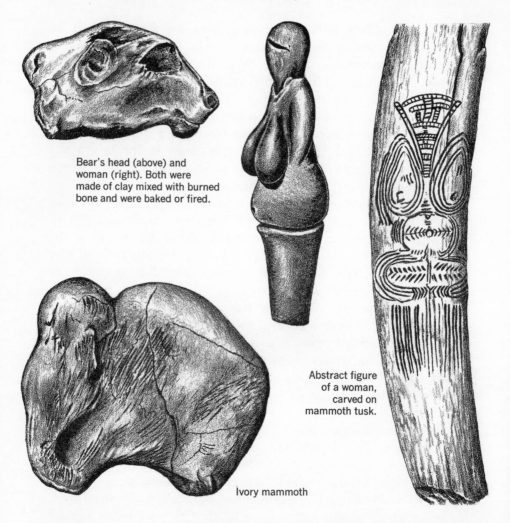

Bear's head (above) and
woman (right). Both were
made of clay mixed with burned
bone and were baked or fired.

Abstract figure
of a woman,
carved on
mammoth tusk.

Ivory mammoth

Works of art made by mammoth-hunters. The baked clay figures are some
of the world's oldest known ceramics.

then, however, someone scratched a design on a bone or ivory tool,
and one artistic priest or magician carved a mammoth in ivory. A still
more inventive priest made the world's first ceramics by mixing wet
clay with powdered, burned bone, modeling figures of animals and
women, and baking them in a simple kiln. In time this priest abandoned his home in such haste that he left half-formed models on the
dirt floor near the present village of Dolní Věstonice.

Near Předmostí, on what was to become Chromatschek's farm, another priest scratched lines, curves, and ovals on a piece of ivory. The result was a picture of a woman that resembles the work of some modern artists who undertake to present the essential nature or "significant form" of objects rather than their actual shapes.

We cannot say this was the artistic mammoth-hunter's objective, for he could leave no document to tell what he was trying to do. But we need no document to convince us that he had the brain and skill to produce something that can be recognized as beautiful. The mammoth-hunting sculptor had come a long way from the man-ape whose most revolutionary achievement was to choose an antelope's leg bone as a club with which to crack a baboon's skull.

Skull of a plant-eating dinosaur about 30 feet long, of Morrison age. It is in the United States National Museum, Washington, D.C.

19 MUSEUMS AND BOOKS

FOSSILS CAN BE read about and studied in pictures, but they should also be seen. So many museums in North America exhibit significant collections of fossils that we can list only the most notable or those with things of special importance.

The largest and most comprehensive exhibits of fossils in North America are to be found in the *United States National Museum*, whose Natural History Building on the mall in Washington is part of the complex of museums administered by the Smithsonian Institution. Fossil plants and invertebrates are supplemented by dioramas showing how these ancient creatures lived. Vertebrates that are exhibited range from fish through amphibians and reptiles (including dinosaur skeletons) to birds and mammals.

The *American Museum of Natural History*, Seventy-ninth Street and Central Park West, New York City, shows superb collections of fossil fish, amphibians, early reptiles, and mammals, as well as a great series of bones, skulls, and mounted skeletons representing both orders of dinosaurs. The *Carnegie Museum*, Schenley Park, Pittsburgh, displays both invertebrate and vertebrate fossils, including huge dinosaurs and fine mammals from the West. Also modern dioramas.

In the *Chicago Museum of Natural History*, Grant Park, Chicago, exhibits range from plants to man, with life-size group restorations of Coal-age plants and insects, marine invertebrates, titanotheres and associated mammals, and various stages of man. Most of the last are in a special ground-floor gallery far from the halls devoted to fossils in general. Other major museums and their offerings are:

Denver Museum of Natural History, City Park, Denver. General exhibit of fossils from the West, including fine dinosaurs and mammals, some of which were killed by early man.

Los Angeles County Museum, Exposition Park, Los Angeles. Pleistocene fossils from the world-famous tar pits and an evolutionary series of horses. The museum also maintains an exhibit on the tar beds of Hancock Park, with life-size models of several ancient mammals.

Milwaukee Public Museum, Wisconsin Avenue at Eighth Street, Milwaukee. A general exhibit, carefully planned to explain fossils to visitors.

National Museum of Canada, Ottawa. Plants, invertebrates and vertebrates, especially of Canada. Fine bird-hipped dinosaurs.

Nebraska State Museum, University of Nebraska, Lincoln. A fine series of vertebrates (especially mammals) from the Great Plains, including many things not to be seen elsewhere. There is also a stegosaur skeleton.

New York State Museum, Education Building, Albany. A comprehensive exhibit of New York fossils, from marine algae to mammals. Excellent dioramas of invertebrates; rocks and fossils of a Devonian forest backed by a painted restoration, and a life-size model of a mastodon beside its skeleton.

Peabody Museum of Yale University, New Haven, Connecticut. A modern general museum; fossils range from plants to mammals. Dinosaurs include the finest apatosaur skeleton as well as bird-hips.

Royal Ontario Museum, Bloor Street, Toronto. A comprehensive exhibit of fossils, with especially fine dinosaurs from the Red Deer Badlands.

Size alone does not make an exhibit worth while; one specimen may reward the visitor who is really interested. Thus the *Academy of Natural Sciences,* Nineteenth Street and The Parkway, Philadelphia, shows bones of the first dinosaur found in North America, as well as a helmeted duckbill (*Corythosaurus*) from Alberta. The *Amherst College Museum,* Amherst, Massachusetts, has the best collection of Triassic dinosaur footprints. The *Badlands National Monument,* on U.S. 16 Alternate, south of Wall, South Dakota, is not a museum but it does show Oligocene deposits more plainly than they appear in any other region. Fine fossils from the Badlands may be seen in the museum of the *South Dakota School of Mines and Technology* at Rapid City and in the museum of *Scotts Bluff National Monument,* near Gering, Nebraska.

The *Buffalo Museum of Science,* Humboldt Park, Buffalo, New York, displays fossils from northwestern New York and a full-scale coral reef group. The *California Academy of Sciences* in Golden Gate Park, San Francisco, displays some western fossils. So does the *Santa*

Barbara Museum, in that city; its most unusual specimen is a very large toothed bird of Tertiary age.

The *Cleveland Museum of Natural History* is famous for its fossil fish of Late Devonian age, some of which show carbonized flesh. *Dinosaur National Monument,* near Jensen, Utah, includes famous collecting localities for lizard-hipped Morrison dinosaurs. A unique museum is built around bones that still lie in steeply tilted sandstones. South of Florissant, Colorado, are two petrified forests where erect redwood stumps may be examined and photographed. They are larger and more numerous than stumps in *Yellowstone National Park. Ginkgo Petrified Forest State Park* (U.S. 10 west of Vantage, Washington) offers both a museum and logs out-of-doors and in beds of volcanic rock. *Petrified Forest National Monument,* both north and south of U.S. 66 near Holbrook, Arizona, combines a small but good museum with a rich natural display of Triassic logs.

The *Exhibit Museum of the University of Michigan,* Ann Arbor, has a duckbilled dinosaur, fine Permian and Triassic vertebrates, varied invertebrates, and excellent dioramas. The famous *Museum of Comparative Zoology* at Harvard University in Cambridge, Massachusetts, displays selected invertebrates and vertebrates, including Permian reptiles and the giant short-necked plesiosaur from Australia. The geological museum in Guyot Hall of *Princeton University,* Princeton, New Jersey, shows many vertebrates, including a mounted allosaur. Another is displayed in the geological museum of the *University of Utah,* in Salt Lake City. The *Texas Memorial Museum* at the University of Texas, Austin, displays fine dinosaur footprints and other fossils.

BOOKS

Books about fossils range from very simple volumes for children to technical treatises. A good textbook of earth history, with much about fossils, is *Historical Geology,* second edition, by Carl O. Dunbar (New York: John Wiley, 1960). *The Vertebrate Story,* by Alfred S. Romer (University of Chicago Press, 1959) is a readable work dealing with both fossil and living vertebrates. *Search for the Past,* by James R. Beerbower (Englewood Cliffs, New Jersey: Prentice-Hall, 1960) is a textbook on general paleontology that gives special attention to the origin of species, evolution, and similar problems. *Time, Life, and Man,* by R. A. Stirton (New York: John Wiley, 1959; also a paperback) is a comprehensive and well-written textbook that is not technical.

Readers who want to identify fossils will usually use technical books. The most general of these is *Index Fossils of North America*, by Hervey W. Shimer and Robert R. Shrock (New York: John Wiley, 1944). Short introductions to invertebrate fossils are published by many state geological surveys.

History of Paleontology

Human beings took a long time to admit that fossils once were alive, and still longer to realize their meaning. Several books tell portions of this story:

Fenton, Carroll Lane and Mildred Adams Fenton. *Giants of Geology* (Garden City, New York: Doubleday & Company, 1952; also a paperback). Chapters 2, 7, 10, 13, 16, and 17 deal with fossils and men who discovered them.

Miller, Hugh. *The Old Red Sandstone* (various editions and dates). Miller was a great collector and a fine writer; this, his most famous book, was a scientific best seller for many years, and its influence extended into the 1900s.

Moore, Ruth E. *Man, Time, and Fossils* (New York: Alfred A. Knopf, 1953). The evolutionary story told by fossils, traced in the work of outstanding paleontologists.

Books Describing Fossils

Augusta, Josef. *A Book of Mammoths* (London: Paul Hamlyn, 1962); *Prehistoric Animals* (same, 1960); *Prehistoric Reptiles and Birds* (same, 1961); *Prehistoric Sea Monsters* (same, 1964). Handsome volumes illustrated, partly in color, by Z. Burian. They contain many restorations not found elsewhere, and their short texts provide a surprising amount of information.

Colbert, Edwin H. *The Dinosaur Book*, second edition (New York: McGraw-Hill Book Company, 1951); *Dinosaurs* (New York: E. P. Dutton & Company, 1961). The former is a handsomely illustrated, non-technical book on fossil reptiles in general. The latter is the most up-to-date and comprehensive book about dinosaurs now available in English.

Fenton, Carroll Lane and Mildred Adams Fenton. *The Fossil Book* (Garden City, New York: Doubleday & Company, 1958). A large but non-technical book for adults, abundantly illustrated. It traces the history of life, at the same time describing the principal groups of plants and animals. Many important species are illustrated and named.

Glaessner, Martin F. "Pre-Cambrian Animals." *Scientific American*, Vol. 204 (March 1961), pp. 72–78. Not a book but an article that describes and illustrates Late Precambrian animals of Australia.

Ransom, J. E. *Fossils in America* (New York: Harper & Row, 1964). The main groups of fossils, how to collect them, their geologic background, and lists of outstanding localities throughout the United States. Some entries are erroneous.

Simpson, George G. *Horses* (New York: Oxford University Press, 1951; also a paperback). A general and authoritative semi-technical book on horses and their relatives.

Ancient Man

Augusta, Josef. *Prehistoric Man* (London: Paul Hamlyn, 1960). Like other books written by Professor Augusta and illustrated by Z. Burian, this handsome volume contains many unusual restorations. Its account of Czech mammoth-hunters is especially useful.

Cornwall, I. W. *The Making of Man* (New York: E. P. Dutton & Company, 1961). This children's book offers a compact survey of ancient man and his predecessors which may be used by anyone. The author is an eminent British prehistorian.

Dart, Raymond A. and Dennis Craig. *Adventures with the Missing Link* (New York: Harper & Row, 1959). Professor Dart's own account of his work with man-apes and his ideas about them.

Howells, William. *Mankind in the Making* (Garden City, New York: Doubleday & Company, 1959). A non-technical survey emphasizing skeletal remains, not tools.

Leakey, Louis S. B. "Finding the World's Earliest Man." *National Geographic*, Vol. 118 (September 1960), pp. 420–35. "Exploring 1,750,000 Years into Man's Past." Same, Vol. 120 (October 1961), pp. 564–89. "Adventures in the Search for Man." Same, Vol. 123, (January 1963), pp. 132–52. Superbly illustrated accounts of the Leakeys' discoveries. The second article deals with apes and ape-men.

Macgowan, Kenneth and Joseph A. Hester, Jr. *Early Man in the New World,* revised edition (Garden City, New York: Doubleday & Company, Anchor Books, 1962). An excellent paperback on a subject not discussed in this book.

Books for Boys and Girls

Dickerson, A. *First Book of Prehistoric Animals* (New York: Franklin Watts, 1954). For readers under twelve.

Fenton, Carroll Lane. *Life Long Ago* (New York: The John Day Company, 1964) and *Prehistoric World* (same, 1954). The first of these is a general book on fossils for readers of nine to twelve or fourteen years. The second, a small volume, deals mostly with vertebrates.

Fenton, Carroll Lane and Mildred Adams Fenton. *Prehistoric Zoo* (Garden City, New York: Doubleday & Company, 1959) and *In Prehistoric Seas* (same, 1962). The former compares fossil vertebrates with living types; the latter reviews marine fossils, from algae to whales. Both books are written in rhythmic prose.

Scheele, William E. *The First Mammals* (New York: World Publishing Company, 1955). An account of many mammals besides the first ones; for readers over twelve.

GLOSSARY

Abbevillian. A name which, in Europe, has replaced *Chellean.* The latter is still used in Africa.

Adaptation. Any structure or function that fits a living thing to its surroundings or way of life.

Agnaths. Primitive fishlike creatures that had no jaws and apparently no paired fins.

Algae. A great variety of simple plants and plantlike things such as seaweeds.

Amber. Fossil resin from ancient trees; it often contains insects.

Ammonoids. Extinct cephalopods whose shells contain bent or crumpled septa. Ammonoids were commonest in the Mesozoic Era.

Amphibians. Vertebrates that usually have four legs, lay soft eggs that develop in water, and breathe with gills while they are young. Some highly specialized forms have lost one or more of these characteristics. Frogs and salamanders are typical amphibians.

Ape-man. Same as *Pithecanthropus.*

Apes. This term usually means anthropoid apes, which are manlike mammals that still do not walk erect, talk, or possess brains as large as those of human beings. Teeth, skull, jaws, and bones of the hips and limbs also differ from those of man.

Australopithecus. Small man-apes of Early Ice-age Africa.

Barrier. Any natural feature that keeps living things from spreading to other parts of the earth. The sea is a barrier to land animals; mountains are barriers to lowland creatures.

Belemnoids. Extinct torpedo- or dart-shaped cephalopods with ten arms and small shells and other hard parts that were covered by skin.

Bird-hips. Ornithischian dinosaurs.

Birds. Feathered vertebrates whose forelegs have become wings.

Blastoids. Echinoderms with stalks and nutlike or bud-shaped bodies covered by a few thick plates.

Bone. One of the parts of a vertebrate skeleton, even if it consists of cartilage. Also the hard material of bones.

Brachiopods. Marine animals whose shells have two parts, or valves, which never are similar. Bodies differ greatly from those of clams.

Calcite. Limy material found in corals, shells, crinoids, and so on. It is identical with the principal material in limestone.

Carbonization. Incomplete decay that leaves the carbon that was once in leaves, flesh, skin, and so on. Many fossil plants have been carbonized; so have some fish and reptiles.

Carnivores. In general, animals that eat meat or other animals. The carnivores (or Carnivora), however, are a group of meat-eating mammals that have four or five toes on each foot and sharp teeth, and usually—but not always—possess claws.

Cartilage. Soft, translucent material found in many vertebrate skeletons. As animals grow old, cartilage may be replaced by bone.

Cell. A small structure made up of living material; also the wall of hard, often woody material that may cover it.

Cephalopods. Highly developed mollusks with large eyes and horny beaks surrounded by fleshy arms that catch food.

Chellean. An ancient stage or type of tool-making, characterized by crudely chipped knives, scrapers, and blunt "hand axes," which probably were used to dig roots, skin large animals, and chop meat. Later hand axes were more carefully chipped and were pointed at one end.

Chromosomes. Structures which contain the genes, or tiny particles, that control heredity. Fossil chromosomes are very rare.

Corals. Soft-bodied marine animals that often build stony supports. Corals are often, but wrongly, called insects.

Crinoids. Echinoderms with many plates on the body and prominent arms that usually branch. Most crinoid bodies are attached to the top of jointed stalks.

Cystoids. Primitive echinoderms whose bodies usually are covered with many small plates. Most cystoids possess stalks.

Dinosaurs. Two groups (orders) of Mesozoic reptiles, many of which became very large. See *Saurischians* and *Ornithischians*.

Echinoderms. Marine animals whose skins contain plates or spines of calcite. Crinoids, starfish, and sea urchins are echinoderms.

Environment. The surroundings of living things, including other animals and plants.

Evolution. The processes by which living things change their hereditary appearance, structure, or functions. In time these changes produce new varieties, species, and larger groups.

Extinction. Any process that causes a species or some other group of living things to die out.

Fish. Three large groups, or classes, of water-dwelling vertebrates. Fish have jaws and fins that are arranged in pairs, as well as others on the back, underside, and tail.

"*Forams*" (actually foraminifers). One-celled protozoans whose soft bodies are protected by hard cases or shells.

Formation. A series of beds or strata that are essentially similar and settled during a limited part of geologic time. Beds in one formation usually contain many identical fossils.

Fossils. Remains or traces of things that lived during ancient geologic times and were buried in rocks that accumulated on the earth's outer portion, or crust.

Ganglion. A cluster or mass of nerve cells that both receives and sends out messages without passing them on to the brain.

Genus. A group of related and generally similar species. To avoid repetition, genera are sometimes referred to as "types."

Gills. Fringed, feathery, or layered organs used to breathe in water. Gills developed at various times and in several ways in different groups of animals.

Herbivores. Plant-eating animals, chiefly vertebrates.

Horn-shells. A non-technical name for cephalopods that build shells around their bodies; the nautiloids and ammonoids.

Ice Age. When capitalized, this term means the Pleistocene Epoch. There were, however, other epochs of cold and glaciation.

Index fossil. A fossil found in the rocks of one epoch or smaller division of time. Once the sequence of rocks and their time-divisions is known, such fossils indicate the geologic age of the beds or formations in which they occur.

Isolation. Anything that separates living things from their relatives or from immigrants. Creatures that are isolated for a long time usually evolve into unusual species and larger groups.

Land bridges. Strips of land that extend between continents or large islands. These strips usually rise at some times and sink at others, thus changing from bridges to barriers.

Larva. An early stage of an animal; it can move about, feed, and do other things, but it is different from adults. A caterpillar is the larva of a butterfly or moth; a tadpole is a larval frog or toad.

Ligament. A band or sheet of tough material that fastens one vertebrate structure to another. Ligaments that connected vertebrae of bird-hipped dinosaurs were stiffened by limy material and therefore are found in fossils.

Lizard-hips. Saurischian dinosaurs.

Living fossils. Living things that have not changed much during periods or even eras and usually are plentiful today.

Lungfish. Fish with lungs and narrow, very flexible paired fins. Many bones in the skeleton have become cartilage; others in the jaws and skull have been lost, and so have ordinary teeth. Lungfish are highly specialized and are not the ancestors of amphibians.

Mammals. Four-limbed vertebrates with warm blood and hair; the females produce milk from glands in the skin. Fossil mammals are recognized by features of their skulls, skeletons, and teeth. Each half of the lower jaw, for example, contains only one bone, though reptilian jaws have several bones.

Mammoths. Extinct elephants of the Pleistocene, or Ice Age. They had high skulls and very long tusks; at least one species was covered with coarse hair and fine wool.

Man. A human being. Some scientists define man as the only tool-making animal. Others list characters that include a large brain, a short face without a projecting muzzle, teeth that are small for the size of the skull, and hip and limb bones adapted to upright life on the ground.

Man-apes. Early Pleistocene creatures that combined the upright position of man with apelike skulls and small brains. Habits probably were manlike.

Mastodons. Mammals closely related to elephants, but with less specialized teeth. One species, the American mastodon, died out only a few thousand years ago.

Mollusks. Clams, oysters, snails, and their relatives. Most of them have shells, but the octopus and some snails do not.

Muscles. Organs that produce movement by shortening the fibers of which they are composed. Most ancient muscles are traced by marks which they left on shells or bones.

Nautiloids. Mollusks whose shells are built on the plan seen in shells of *Nautilus.* Nautiloids were most abundant during the Paleozoic Era.

Neanderthal man. An ancient human species characterized by a long, low skull, chinless face, and heavy bones in arms and legs. These people lived in many regions during the Pleistocene Epoch.

Organism. A plant, animal, or any other living thing.

Ornithischians. Dinosaurs whose hipbones resemble those of birds.

Paleontology. The science that deals with fossils.

Paranthropus. A group, or genus, of large man-apes that liked lake shores and moist plains. *Paranthropus* lived in Africa during Early Pleistocene times.

Pithecanthropus. A genus of erect but rather small-brained men of apelike appearance that ranged from Africa to Europe, China, and Java during the Middle Pleistocene. They made stone tools, including those of Chellean, or Abbevillian, type. Often called *Homo erectus.*

Proconsul. A genus of Early Miocene apes of Africa; they seem to have been the ancestors of chimpanzees and gorillas as well as man-apes.

Protozoans. One-celled creatures often called "first animals," though they seem to belong to other kingdoms. Most fossil protozoans are "forams."

Red Beds. When capitalized, this term means delta deposits of Late Pennsylvanian and Early Permian age in Texas and Oklahoma. However, dark-red sands and muds were deposited at other times and in other regions. Thus there are Devonian red beds (usually not capitalized) in Pennsylvania, Triassic red beds in New England, and so on.

Reptiles. Vertebrates with bony skeletons and dry, usually scaly skins. Eggs develop on land or in the mother's body; the young breathe with lungs, not gills. Teeth usually have only one point; each half of the lower jaw contains more than one bone, in contrast to the jaw of mammals.

Saurischians. Dinosaurs whose hipbones resemble those of lizards and crocodiles. Saurischians include the largest dinosaurs.

Segment. Part of a body that is marked off or separated from parts before and behind. An earthworm has many similar segments; those of trilobites may be similar or may differ in size or shape.

Septum. A dividing wall or partition. In this book the term refers to partitions built behind the bodies of horn-shelled cephalopods.

Shell. The hard covering of a body or structure. In this book the word is used for hard coverings that cannot be shed and replaced by a new one. A horn-shell is a good example.

Skin-crust. A covering formed upon the skin of an animal. It can be shed and replaced by a new one; a crab's "shell" is an example. Many skin-crusts never become hard.

Species. One kind of living thing. A group of similar species that are related makes up a genus.

Spore. A cell that can develop into a new living thing without being fertilized, or combining with a different cell. Spores are especially important among plants such as ferns.

Suture. The line along which two hard parts join. The sutures of horn-shells show where septa join the shells.

Thecodonts. Extinct reptiles that were the ancestors of lizard-hipped and bird-hipped dinosaurs, as well as phytosaurs. Thecodonts or closely related reptiles also were the ancestors of crocodiles, pterosaurs, and birds.

Thorax. The part of an animal behind its head or a headlike section such as the cephalon of a trilobite.

Trilobites. Extinct animals whose bodies were made up of jointed sections and were divided into *lobes* by grooves that ran lengthwise across the segments. The name means "three-lobed ones."

Vertebrates. In everyday language, vertebrates are animals with backbones, or series of vertebrae. Actually, some vertebrae are only partly formed; many consist of cartilage, not bone; others are not preserved in fossils. Some scientists call an animal a vertebrate if it has a skull or a case of bone or cartilage around the brain. Another name for such animals is *craniates.*

Zinjanthropus. A large African man-ape with powerful jaw muscles, indicated by a crest on top of the skull. The creature may belong to the genus *Paranthropus.*

INDEX

with pronunciations

Pronunciations of most names are given in the singular, even though the names themselves may be plural: Titanotheres (TY' tan o THEER) for example. Exceptions are terms whose singular form differs considerably from the plural; for these the plural pronunciation is followed by the singular, as in Ganglia (GANG gli a; GANG gli on).

Some words have one pronunciation as formal names but another when they are turned into English. Formal names usually are italicized in text and are pronounced in "English" Latin: *Ammonites* (AM' mo NY teez) for example. But the same name becomes ammonites (AM mon ites) in English.

Heavy type (**70** instead of 70) indicates pages on which illustrations appear, even if the subjects of those illustrations is dealt with in the text on those same pages.

Date Due

DEC 1 5					
OCT 6					
1/98 Perreault					